Programmed learning aid for

BUSINESS
and
ECONOMIC
STATISTICS

Programmed learning aid for

BUSINESS
and
ECONOMIC
STATISTICS

ROBERT D. MASON
Associate Professor of Statistics
The University of Toledo

Coordinating editor
ROGER H. HERMANSON
The University of Maryland

LEARNING SYSTEMS COMPANY
A division of Richard D. Irwin, Inc., Homewood, Illinois
Canadian distribution through
Irwin-Dorsey Limited, Georgetown, Ontario

Library of Congress Catalog Card No. 70–83126

Printed in the United States of America

234567890K8765432

Foreword

Students often have found reviewing for examinations a dull and tedious process. This PLAID series was created to provide the user with an effective, efficient, and interesting means of accomplishing this task. It applies the powerful tool of programmed learning to the subject matter areas comprising business and economics.

The method of programming is easy to use and has the following advantages:

1. Correct response to concepts reviewed is *reinforced immediately*.
2. Incorrect interpretation of concepts reviewed is *corrected immediately*.
3. The reader is kept *active* in the review process and increases his comprehension.
4. The method is *fun* to use. It makes reviewing seem like a game.

The PLAID for Statistics was used in test edition form by a large number of students who were enthusiastic in their praise of its effectiveness. It can be used as a supplement with almost any textbook designed for use in an introductory course in statistics.

The author is an excellent teacher, has taught statistics for a number of years, and is "student oriented." His continual concern in developing his PLAID was with simplicity of presentation so as to effectively communicate the essential subject matter of statistics to the reader. I'm sure you will agree that he has done so.

ROGER H. HERMANSON
Coordinating Editor

Preface

This Programmed Learning Aid provides a means of self-review of the techniques studied in most introductory courses in statistics. While many of the illustrations are business oriented, the statistical methods are equally applicable in other areas such as the social sciences, education, and engineering. This PLAID also can be used effectively by students entering a graduate studies program, executives participating in management development programs, and persons working or studying in marketing, accounting, and related fields.

The PLAID is designed to be used as a supplement to your textbook. It is organized into chapters. The chapters are in a logical sequence, but the sequence can be altered to that of any statistics textbook. Each chapter is subdivided into a number of short segments called frames. In each frame the reader tests his comprehension of the material by answering questions that are presented. The answer is always given in the margin.

The following example illustrates the technique used. Before reading the material presented in the frame, cover the answers given in the margin. Now read the material and answer the questions.

1 ─────────────────────────────

The arithmetic mean is one of the most commonly used averages. It is found by summing all of the items and dividing the sum by the total number of items. For example, the hourly wage rates of four men are $7, $4, $6, and $3 respectively. The arithmetic mean hourly wage is $5, found by $\dfrac{\$7 + \$4 + \$6 + \$3}{4}$.

The monthly income of the five employees of the Ace Stamping Company are $400, $350, $600, $750 and $400 respectively. The total monthly payroll is $_____, and the arithmetic mean monthly income is $_____.

$2,500

$500, found by $\dfrac{\$2,500}{5}$

A distinctive feature of this programmed learning aid is the Final Self-Review Examination (with answers) found at the end of each chapter. By answering the 10 review questions, an additional evaluation can be made of how well the concepts in the chapter were understood. Other features of the PLAID include a glossary of terms and formulas found in the Appendix and a Topical Outline of Course Content as contained in basic books in this field.

Toledo, Ohio   ROBERT D. MASON

Topical outline of course content

Table of contents

Introduction

1 ———————————————————————————

The word *statistics* has several connotations. In one sense, statistics refers to a collection of numerical data. A perusal of several business magazines revealed these statistics. "A person who has done work beyond a bachelors degree can anticipate a total lifetime income of $587,000 which is more than three times that of an elementary school dropout ($189,000)."[1] From *Forbes*,[2] "But the elderly, who have twice as much money to spend as the teen-agers, are getting scant attention from the marketing men. They are a $40 billion market." *Business Week*[3] reports that "It was a very good year for the nation's breadwinners. The gross national product leaped 9% last year, providing jobs for nearly 1.4 million more people." In this use, statistics (a plural noun) refers to all the various data cited, such as the lifetime income of $587,000, employment of 1.4 million, and so on.

The word *statistics* is also used to identify the science of collecting, organizing, presenting, analyzing, and interpreting data. The Civil Service Commission defines statistics as "a body of techniques for acquiring accurate knowledge from incomplete information, a scientific system for the collection, organization, analysis, interpretation, and presentation of information which can be stated in numerical form."

Note from the foregoing definition that statisticians work with incomplete data. An order for steel wire might specify that the average tensile strength of the wire must be 10,000 pounds per square inch or more. Out of harsh economic necessity, a decision to accept or reject an incoming shipment of the wire must be made on, say, eight pieces selected at random. Since a test for tensile strength destroys the wire, checking all of the incoming wires would not be feasible. The management of another company must make a decision whether or not to market a newly developed molasses-coated cereal based on incomplete information about consumer preference. Sending introductory test packages to nearly 200 million consumers in the United States would be very costly and time-consuming. The usual procedure is to conduct a product test using a panel of about 2,000 families. Inventory control, auditing, plant location, and sales forecasting are but a few other areas in business where decisions are made based on incomplete information.

Because complete information is not available, there is usually some uncertainty involved in making most decisions. This means that there is a risk of making a wrong decision. Based on the sample of eight pieces of steel wire, the quality control engineer might accept the incoming shipment of wire when it should have been rejected. If a decision is made to market the molasses-coated cereal based on the test-panel results, there is a chance that the cereal will not be accepted by the public.

Statistical methods are used extensively in areas other than business such as medical research, education, economics, insurance, psychology, the social sciences, and so on. Economists, for example, are interested in measuring the extent of inflation and projecting the demand for labor. Research is being done in education on the effectiveness

[1] *U.S. News and World Report*, January 6, 1969, p. 73.
[2] *Forbes*, January 15, 1969, p. 22.
[3] *Business Week*, January 11, 1969, p. 61.

of newly developed teaching devices and techniques. Medical research is concerned with assessing new vaccines. Demographers use statistical methods in studying and projecting population growth and birth rates.

2 ———————————————————————

DESCRIPTIVE STATISTICS AND INDUCTIVE STATISTICS

One facet of the study of statistical methods is designated as *descriptive statistics*. To illustrate, the subcontracts totaling $1,669 million for the Lockheed L–1011, the 250 passenger tri-jet airbus are:

Company	Amount of Subcontract (Millions of Dollars)
Rolls-Royce, Ltd.	$ 900
Aerostructures Division	575
Avco Corp.	
Menasco Mfg. Co.	90
Hamilton Standard Division	60
United Aircraft Corp.	
Collins Radio Co. and Astronic Division	40
Lear Siegler, Inc.	
B. F. Goodrich Co.	4
Total	$1,669

Source: *Business Week*, September 7, 1968, p. 38.

An analysis of the statistics merely reveals that Rolls-Royce, Ltd., received the largest subcontract, B. F. Goodrich the smallest, and so on. Another facet of statistics is called *inductive statistics* or *statistical inference*, which deals with sample data. In most mass-production industries, it is deemed too expensive to check all the parts manufactured. Quality control engineers at Chevrolet, Toledo Division, select a sample of eight short pinion gears at random every half hour. On the basis of certain averages and other computed statistics, a decision is made about all short pinion gears produced during that 30-minute period. The total group is called a *population* and the few parts selected from the population are called a *sample*.

sample
population

The eight short pinion gears are called a _____, and all the gears produced during the half hour are called the _____.

3 ———————————————————————

Suppose that a sample of 84 shoes were strapped to a special rotary machine and "walked" until a hole appeared in the sole. The average mileage was computed to be 87.3 miles. This sample result is called a sample *statistic*. It was decided to give all the shoes produced during the day (24,568 shoes) a life test, and it was found that the average mileage of the population was 87.5 miles. This figure (87.5) is called a population *parameter*.

The average tensile strength of 10 wires selected at random for an incoming shipment of steel wires was computed to be 14,340 pounds per square inch. The 14,340 psi

statistic
it is associated
with a sample

is called a _____ because _____

_____ .

4

Statistical data is considered as being either *discrete* or *continuous*. Discrete data can only be whole numbers and result from counting persons or items. There are 32 children in the fifth grade, and the inventory revealed that there are 16,854 different items in stock.

These are two examples of _____ data because the figures are the result of _____.

discrete
counts

Continuous data can have fractional values and result from measuring. That is, the measurement given could be further subdivided if more precise instruments were used. Three pieces of steel had lengths of 1.001, 1.000 and 1.003 inches respectively. This is an example of _____ data because _____.

continuous
the figures are
the result of measuring

Final Self-Review Examination

First, answer all of the questions. Then check your answers against those given at the end of this chapter. Scoring: 10 problems × 10 points each = 100 possible points.

5. Sales last month were $1,215,672.42. This facet of statistics which merely describes the situation is called _____ statistics.

6. Based on the sample survey just conducted, it is estimated that the average income in the proposed shopping area is between $9,800 and $9,900. When sample data is used to make statements about the total, the facet of statistics is called _____.

7. Political pollsters (Harris, Gallup, Roper, and others) usually interview about 1,500 potential voters in a pre-election poll out of the millions eligible to vote. The relatively small number (1,500) is called a _____.

8. The total of all of the voters (the millions eligible to vote) is called the _____.

9. Out of the 1,500 selected in the pre-election poll, 900, or 60 percent, indicated that they favored the Republican candidate. Because the figure 60 percent is associated with a sample, it is called a _____.

10. The actual percent when all the voters indicated their preference was 58 percent for the Republican candidate. This figure (58%) is called a _____.

11. There are 58,003 persons in the metropolitan area, and 92 different colors are available. These data are considered (discrete/continuous) _____.

12. The average length of fish caught in the tournament was 12.2 inches, and the length of life of a typical bulb in a traffic signal is 47 months. These data are considered _____.

13. One meaning of the word statistics is _____.

14. Another meaning of the word statistics is _____.

Answers to Final Self-Review Examination

5. descriptive
6. statistical inference or inductive statistics
7. sample
8. population
9. statistic
10. parameter
11. discrete

12. continuous
13. The word *statistics* might refer to a collection of numerical data. For example, there were 720,100 persons unemployed, 56,871,900 were employed, etc.
14. Statistics also refers to the science of collecting, organizing, presenting, analyzing, and interpreting numerical data.

The collection and presentation of statistical data

2

1

COLLECTION OF DATA

The first step toward describing a business phenomena is to collect the necessary statistical data. The source of the business data may be classified as being *internal* or *external*.

Internal data includes statistics on the company's operations, such as sales statistics and production statistics. The machine records department sent the sales manager these sales figures for the previous three months: $987,651.76, $876,598.89, and $1,023,458.92. The source of the data is considered _____.

Statistical data not associated with the operation of the business firm itself is called *external* data. The sales manager of an automobile manufacturer may need data on the number of automobiles in use in the United States by age, in order to make estimates of sales 5, 10, and 15 years from now. This data is considered _____ data.

external

2

There is a vast amount of external business data in published form which can be found in university and public libraries. For example, population data, by age, is collected every 10 years by the Bureau of the Census and published in the *Census of Population*. The sales manager can find the age distribution of motor vehicles in an annual publication called *Automobile Facts and Figures* published by the automobile industry.

The Federal government is the largest publisher of annual, monthly, weekly, and daily statistics. One annual publication of the Department of Commerce, the *Statistical Abstract of the United States*, contains over 1,000 pages of population, price, education, production, and other data which may be of use to economists, marketing analysts, and others. A few annual statistics selected from various tables are:

> 240,747,000 projected population of the United States for 1985.
> 14.3 percent of American families had incomes under $3,000.
> 47,031 persons were arrested for robbery.
>
> Source: U.S. Department of Commerce, *Statistical Abstract of the United States*, 1968, pp. 13, 608, 325.

A few of the monthly publications of the federal government are the *Monthly Labor Review*, the *Survey of Current Business*, and the *Federal Reserve Bulletin*. As the name implies, the *Monthly Labor Review* contains various monthly labor statistics, such as total civilian employment. The *Survey of Current Business* includes the total monthly department store sales and the Wholesale Price Index. The amount of money in circulation last month and the dollar reserves at the various Federal Reserve banks are but two financial series found in the *Federal Reserve Bulletin*. The total number of business

failures can probably be found in the _____.
The total number of persons unemployed last month can be located in the _____
_____ _____ and various monthly financial statistics can be
found in the _____ _____ _____. If a search of these
sources for specific data is unproductive, one or more of the following reference aids
may be consulted. Edwin T. Coman's *Sources of Business Information* has nearly 300
pages of references categorized into foreign trade, marketing, real estate, and so on.
Marian Manley's *Business Information—How to Find and Use It*, the *Business Period-
icals Index*, and the indexes of *The New York Times* and *The Wall Street Journal* are
other reference aids.

Survey of Current Business
Monthly Labor Review

Federal Reserve Bulletin

3

THE QUESTIONNAIRE AS A SOURCE OF DATA

Statistical data regarding the current opinions of consumers toward specific television programs, newly developed foods, political candidates, and so on cannot be
found in published sources. Thus, this type of data must be collected by *personal interview*, by *mail questionnaire*, or by some other means. The Roper, Gallup, and Harris
polls use the personal interview technique almost exclusively. The main advantage of
this technique is the high percentage of response possible. It is usually more expensive,
however, than mailing out questionnaires. Research firms report that the disadvantage
of the mail questionnaire as a tool to collect data is the relatively low percent of response to some questionnaires. Telephone interviews, automatic car counters on high-
ways, and audimeters attached to television sets to record the programs watched are a
few other techniques used to collect numerical data. A major advantage of a personal
interview as a method of collecting data is _____.

high-percent response

The major advantage of the mail questionnaire as a data-collecting technique is

relatively low cost
_____.

4

PRESENTATION OF DATA

Simple line graphs and simple bar graphs.   Either of these two types of graphs can be
used effectively to portray the general trend of sales, production, and the like over a
period of time.

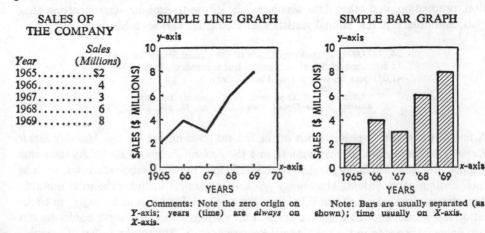

SALES OF
THE COMPANY

Year	Sales (Millions)
1965	$2
1966	4
1967	3
1968	6
1969	8

SIMPLE LINE GRAPH

Comments: Note the zero origin on
Y-axis; years (time) are *always* on
X-axis.

SIMPLE BAR GRAPH

Note: Bars are usually separated (as
shown); time usually on X-axis.

Masses of statistical data from within the company, from published sources, or collected using a personal interview or mail questionnaire are usually not in a meaningful form for analysis. The data should be organized and presented in either *table form* or *chart form* before any analysis and interpretation are made. If precise figures are needed in a report (such as sales figures in the annual report of a company), the data should be presented in a table. If not, a graph (chart) may be preferred to attract the attention of the reader.

In the spaces below, portray the following production series in the form of a simple line graph and a simple bar graph.

PRODUCTION OF A COMPANY	SIMPLE LINE GRAPH	SIMPLE BAR GRAPH
Year — Production (000)		
1964................. 4		
1965................. 3		
1966................. 8		
1967.................12		
1968.................10		
1969.................17		

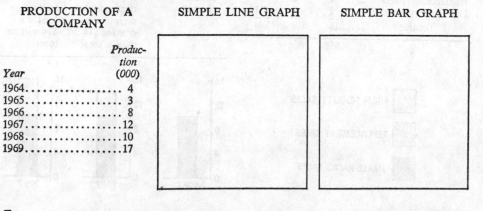

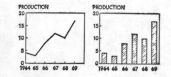

5

Multiple line graph and multiple bar graph. The trend in the exports of two competitors are portrayed graphically. Complete the multiple line graph by plotting the exports of Company B. Use a dashed (- - -) line. Then complete the multiple bar graph by plotting the exports for 1967, 1968, and 1969.

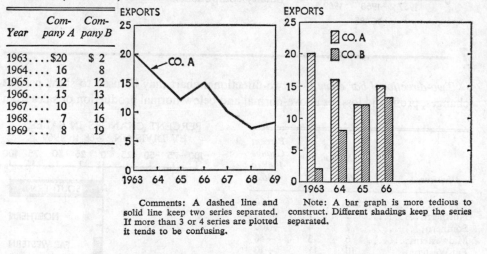

EXPORTS (In Millions)

Year	Company A	Company B
1963....	$20	$ 2
1964....	16	8
1965....	12	12
1966....	15	13
1967....	10	14
1968....	7	16
1969....	8	19

MULTIPLE LINE GRAPH

Comments: A dashed line and solid line keep two series separated. If more than 3 or 4 series are plotted it tends to be confusing.

MULTIPLE BAR GRAPH

Note: A bar graph is more tedious to construct. Different shadings keep the series separated.

EXPORTS

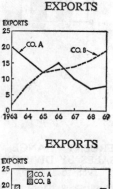

EXPORTS

6

Component bar graph. The sales manager of a company manufacturing small radios, replacement parts, and high-fidelity components wishes to graph the total sales for three years and also the change in each component relative to the total. A component line graph (not shown) or a component bar graph could be used. The steps involved in designing a *component bar graph* are:

Item	Sales (Millions)				To Plot Sales for 1967:		
	1967	1968	1969		Step 1	Step 2	Step 3
Small radios	$10	$ 8	$ 3		Plot sales of $10 million (small radios)	Plot sales of $4 million (replacement parts) on top of radios for $14 million total	Plot sales of $2 million (high-fidelity) on top for a $16 million total
Replacement parts	4	4	4				
High-fidelity parts	2	7	17				
Total	$16	$19	$24				

HIGH FIDELITY SALES

REPLACEMENT SALES

SMALL RADIO SALES

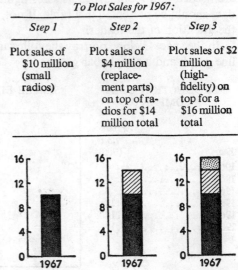

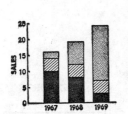

The sales for 1967 (from Step 3) are shown in the adjacent graph. Complete the graph by plotting the sales for 1968 and 1969. The same procedure should be followed, i.e., small radios should be plotted first, then sales of replacement parts plotted on top of radio sales, and finally the sales of high-fidelity components.

7

Two-directional bar chart. A two-directional chart may be used to show percent changes, profit and loss, or above-normal and below-normal production or sales from

PERCENT CHANGE IN SALES BY DIVISION, 1968 to 1969

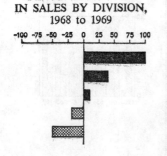

Division	Sales (Millions)		Percent Change 1968 to 1969
	1968	1969	
Eastern	$10	$ 8	−20
Northern	5	7	+40
Southern	2	4	+100
Midwestern	6	3	−50
Far Western	10	11	+10

PERCENT CHANGES IN SALES, BY DIVISION, 1968 to 1969

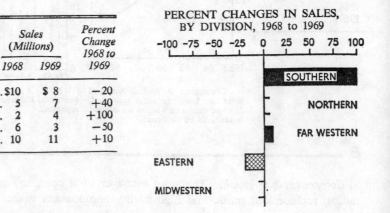
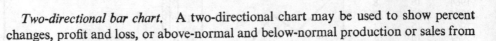

one time period to another time period. For example, the *percent changes* in sales for the five sales divisions from 1968 to 1969 are to be portrayed (not the changes in the dollar amounts). A commonly used technique is to arrange the percent increases shown in the previous table in descending order (+100, +40, and +10 percent), and the percent decreases in ascending order (−20 and −50 percent). These percent changes are then plotted in the same order. Note that the bars go in two directions from zero. Plot the percent changes for the Northern division and the Midwestern division.

The previous graph is called a (b)_____. Based on the graph, which division had the largest percent increase in sales from 1968 to 1969? _____. Which division had the largest percent decrease? _____. This type of graph is especially appropriate to portray _____

_____.

Two-directional bar chart

Southern
Midwestern
percent changes, profit and
  loss, or above-normal and
  below-normal changes.

8 ——————————————————————————————————

Pie graph. If the relative size of the components of the total are to be emphasized, a pie chart is an appropriate graphic tool. For example, from an analysis of Chart A it is readily apparent that labor costs account for almost half of the total costs. The circumference of the circle represents 100 percent. The usual method of drawing a pie chart is to convert the data into percents of the total. As shown, various shadings can be used to separate the components.

**CHART A
COST OF OPERATING
A FIRM**

Using the county income data in the following table, design a pie graph. (Plots can only be approximate.)

SOURCES OF COUNTY INCOME, 1969

Source	Income (Millions)
Property tax	$12
Income tax	6
All other sources	2
Total	$20

one way is:

9 ——————————————————————————————————

The previous graphs were drawn on *arithmetic* paper. Equal distances on arithmetic paper represent equal *amounts*. For example, in the following graph sales increased an equal amount ($1 million) each year.

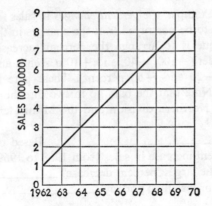

Year	Sales (Millions)
1962	$1
1963	2
1964	3
1965	4
1966	5
1967	6
1968	7
1969	8

It appears that sales have been increasing at a steady rate, but a more thorough study of the actual sales shows that between 1962 and 1963 sales increased 100 percent; the second year, 50 percent (from $2 million to $3 million); the next year, 33⅓ percent ($3 million to $4 million); and so on. Although sales have been rising from year to year, the rate of increase has been _____ _____. Thus, it may be misleading to plot this type of series (an arithmetic progression) on arithmetic graph paper. Now plot the same sales series on *semilogarithmic* graph paper.

decreasing

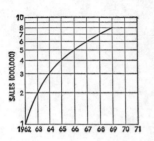

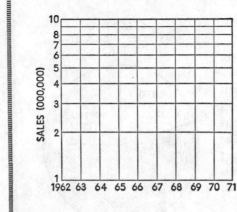

10 _____

The semilogarithmic paper used in the preceding sales illustration is called one-cycle semilogarithmic or ratio paper. Note that the X-axis is evenly spaced and has an arithmetic scaling. The Y-axis is constructed using logarithms. Equal distances on the Y-axis represent equal *percent* changes. The distance between 1 and 2 is the same as between 2 and 4, and also 4 and 8. Each represents a 100 percent increase.

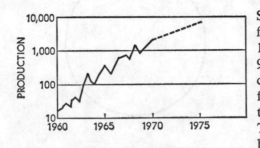

Semilogarithmic paper is very versatile. Suppose production increased drastically from 12 units in 1960 to 6,000 units in 1969 and projected production in 1975 is 9,000 units. The semilogarithmic paper could be designed so that the bottom figure on the Y-axis is 10, the top figure of the first cycle would be 100, as shown. Three-cycle semi-logarithmic paper would be needed to chart the data.

Note on semilog paper that the distance from the bottom of a cycle to the top of a cycle represents a tenfold increase. The bottom number can be any number except zero. The paper can be purchased in one, two, three, four, five, or six cycles.

Suppose exports have increased from $12 million in 1950 to $642 million at the present time. How many cycles would be needed to plot the data? (Assume the bottom number on the *Y*-axis is $10 million) _____. Suppose the debt of a state increased from $122,000 in 1931 to $6 billion at the present time. How many cycles would be needed to plot the data? _____.

2

5

Semilogarithmic paper has other uses, including plotting a *geometric* series. A geometric series increases at a constant rate, such as 12 percent each period. Which paper to use depends on what the statistician wants to emphasize. If the *amount* of change from year to year is most important, _____ paper should be used. If the *rate* of growth is more important, _____ paper should be used.

arithmetic
semilogarithmic

Final Self-Review Examination

First, answer all of the questions. Then check your answers against those given at the end of this chapter. Scoring: 10 problems × 10 points each.

11. Data found within a firm is classified as _____ _____ data.

12. Total employment in the United States last month, employment in manufacturing, the number of workers in the United States quitting their jobs, and other monthly statistics on the labor force can be found in a monthly publication of the federal government called the_____.

13. The number of $2 bills in circulation, money turnover, and other monthly financial statistics can be found in a monthly publication entitled _____ _____ _____.

14. If the search of publications such as the *Statistical Abstract of the United States* does not uncover the data being sought, various reference aids may be consulted. One reference aid is _____.

15. Statistical data may be presented for analysis and interpretation in _____ form or _____ form.

16. Present the following sales data in a simple line graph. Label.

Year	Sales (Millions)
1964	$ 3
1965	7
1966	2
1967	6
1968	8
1969	11

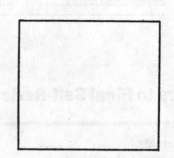

17. Present the following data in a component bar graph. The objective is to show *for each year* the sales of each department as a component of the total. Label. Use the shading given for each department.

Department	Sales ($000) 1968	1969
Suit	$20	$ 9
Shoe	4	4
TV	30	57

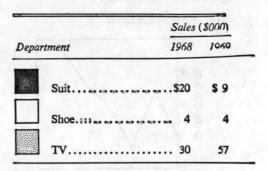

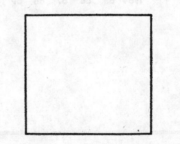

18. The production scheduling department wants to show graphically that the production of some parts increased percentagewise from 1968 to 1969 and others decreased percentagewise. Present the *percent* increases and decreases in a two-directional bar graph. Label.

Part	Production (000)	
	1968	*1969*
Beer bottles................	500	600
Aspirin bottles.............	100	70
Medical bottles............	1,000	1,600
Perfume bottles............	2,000	1,000
Experimental bottles........	10	9

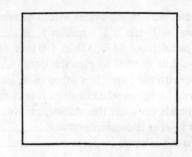

19. Graphs in business and economics are usually drawn on paper having either an _____ _____ scale or a _____ scale.

20. Exports of a company increased from $127,000 in 1951 to $191 million this past year. To portray these export figures, how many cycle semilogarithmic (ratio) paper would be needed? _____

Answers to Final Self-Review Examination

11. internal
12. *Monthly Labor Review*
13. *Federal Reserve Bulletin*
14. Possible answers are: Index of *The New York Times* or *The Wall Street Journal; Business Periodical Index;* Manley, *Business Information —How to Find and Use It;* Coman, *Sources of Business Information.*

15. table, or graphic form
16.

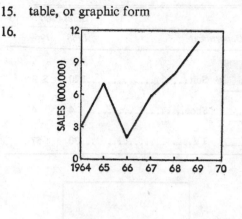

17.

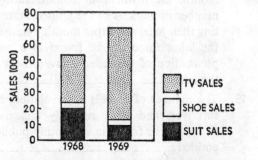

18. PERCENT CHANGE IN THE PRODUCTION OF BOTTLES 1968 to 1969

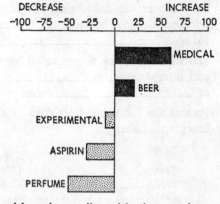

19. arithmetic, semilogarithmic or ratio
20. four

Frequency distributions

1 ──

Business problems involve a large mass of quantitative data which must be organized into some meaningful form before any analysis and interpretation can be made. One commonly used form is the *frequency distribution*. Recall that two types of variables were discussed; namely, discrete and continuous. Frequency distribution analysis is usually concerned with continuous data.

THE ARRAY AND TALLIES

A survey of computer operators in small firms revealed the following monthly incomes (after taxes).

$810	$ 725	$810	$ 875	$850	$ 925	$ 845	$ 880	$750
600	750	790	1,180	850	910	835	1,000	950
875	800	784	800	605	550	1,065	1,175	
770	1,050	987	810	700	890	720	920	
950	545	550	792	825	990	850	900	
850	680	750	600	650	1,075	890	1,050	

The data which are in *ungrouped* form are difficult to analyze, i.e., to determine the low and high incomes, and a central point of concentration, if any. In order to analyze the incomes it is essential, therefore, to organize the data which are in _____ form into a *grouped* form called a *frequency distribution*.

ungrouped

There are two methods of organizing the ungrouped data into a frequency distribution. The first requires setting up an *array* and then *tallying* the incomes into the array. An array is a simple listing of all the monthly incomes arranged in order from the lowest income to the highest income, or vice versa. It was arbitrarily decided to start with the lowest monthly income. The lowest income is _____. All possible monthly incomes would then be listed in ascending order. Next, the income of each computer operator would be tallied opposite the appropriate amount. See example.

Income	Tally
$545	/
546	
547	
548	
549	
550	/ /
etc.	

$545

2 ──

THE CLASSES AND THE CLASS INTERVAL

To make a frequency distribution from the array and tallies shown in the previous frame, the incomes could be arbitrarily grouped into *classes* with an interval of, say, $100. The $100 is called the *class interval*. The class interval is merely the range of monthly incomes for each class. A convenient way to determine it is to find the difference between the *lower limits* of two adjoining classes. If the classes were $500 up to $600, $600 up to $700 and so on, the difference between the two lower limits of $500 and $600 is $100 (the class interval). The monthly income grouping of $500 up to $600

class
does not

is called a ______________. Note that it (does/does not) ______________ contain the income of $600. The tallies in each of the income classes would then be counted to construct a frequency distribution.

3

A second, or alternative method of organizing the ungrouped data into a frequency distribution is usually less time-consuming. The class interval and the classes are determined first, and the data are tallied directly into the classes. (See the following exhibit.) Fill in the blanks.

17
8
50

Monthly Incomes after Taxes	*Tallies*	*Number of Operators*
$ 500 up to $ 600	///	3
600 up to 700	~~////~~	5
700 up to 800	~~////~~ ~~////~~	10
800 up to 900	~~////~~ ~~////~~ ~~////~~ //	—
900 up to 1,000	~~////~~ ///	—
1,000 up to 1,100	~~////~~	5
1,100 up to 1,200	//	2
Total		—

4

$800 up to $900
$500
$1,200

Now an analysis of the incomes of the computer operators can be made. Referring to the frequency distribution, the largest concentration of incomes is in the ______________ up to ______________ class. Based on the frequency distribution, the lowest monthly income is about ______________ and the highest about ______________.

5

class interval
$500 lower
$600 upper
3
50 $100

If the classes were 14 up to 18 pounds, 18 up to 22 pounds, and so forth, the distance between the classes, called the ______________ is 4 pounds. The limits for the 14 up to 18 pound class are 14 pounds for the *lower limit* and 18 pounds for the *upper limit*. If there were 5 fish weighing between 14 and 18 pounds, the number of fish (5) is called the *frequency*.

Referring to the distribution of monthly incomes of computer operators in frame #3, the limits of the lowest income class are ______________ for the ______________ limit and ______________ for the ______________ limit. The frequency for that $500 up to $600 class is ______________. The total of the frequencies is ______________. The class interval used is ______________.

6

$100

The income classes could have been stated in a number of ways, such as $500–$599.99, $500 through $599.99, and $500 up to but not including $600. The interval between the classes (the class interval) in each of these illustrations is ______________.

7 ───

OTHER CRITERIA FOR THE CONSTRUCTION OF A FREQUENCY
DISTRIBUTION

In practice, the total number of classes usually varies from a minimum of 5 to a
maximum of 15. Too few or too many classes might not reveal the essential characteristics of the data. For example, if the incomes of the computer operators were organized into just two classes:

Monthly Incomes	Number of Operators
$500 up to $ 850	26
850 up to 1,200	24

An analysis of the frequency distribution (would/would not) _____
____ reveal much about the income pattern of the computer operators in the small
firms.

would not

8 ───

Whenever possible, the interval between all of the classes in a frequency distribution
should be equal. Unequal class intervals present problems when graphing and computing averages and other statistical measures. The class interval in the following distribution of tensile strengths is (equal/unequal) _____,

unequal

Tensile Strength of Wires (In Pounds per Square Inch)	Number of Wires
Under 12,000..	6
12,000 up to 15,000................................	18
15,000 up to 20,000................................	7
20,000 up to 50,000................................	4
50,000 pounds and over...........................	2
	37

9 ───

The distribution of tensile strengths in frame #8 is also an illustration of a frequency
distribution with *open-end* classes. One open-end class is "under 12,000 pounds" and
the other is _____. The distribution of tensile strengths
would be difficult to graph, and measures such as the arithmetic mean and standard
deviation studied in subsequent chapters could not be computed.

50,000 pounds and over

Finally, the class interval selected should result in but one point of concentration in
contrast to two or more peaks.

As noted in Chapter 2, it is often desirable to graph quantitative data in order to
gain the attention of the reader. Also, a graph may reveal certain relationships which
might not be clearly discernible from an analysis of a frequency distribution table.
Three graphs associated with frequency distributions are the *histogram*, the *frequency
polygon*, and the *cumulative frequency polygon* or *ogive*.

10

THE HISTOGRAM

The income distribution of the computer operators is used again to illustrate the construction of a histogram. Note that three operators earned between $500 and $600 after taxes. Vertical lines are drawn from $500 and from $600 on the X-axis to 3 on the Y-axis. This area is enclosed to form a bar. (See exhibit.) Next, a bar is drawn to represent the five men who earned between $600 and $700. Complete the histogram.

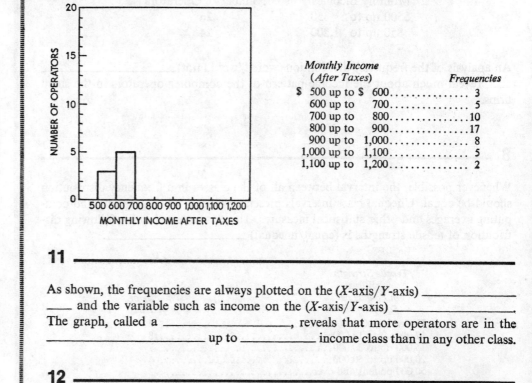

Monthly Income (After Taxes)	Frequencies
$ 500 up to $ 600	3
600 up to 700	5
700 up to 800	10
800 up to 900	17
900 up to 1,000	8
1,000 up to 1,100	5
1,100 up to 1,200	2

11

Y–axis
X–axis
histogram
$800 up to $900

As shown, the frequencies are always plotted on the (X-axis/Y-axis) _____ ____ and the variable such as income on the (X-axis/Y-axis) _____. The graph, called a _____, reveals that more operators are in the _____ up to _____ income class than in any other class.

12

THE FREQUENCY POLYGON

The frequency distribution may also be portrayed graphically in the form of a *frequency polygon.* The *midpoints* of each class are used to represent the typical income of the computer operators in that class. For example, the midpoint of the $500 up to $600 class (frame #10) is _____. This mid-value is assumed to be the typical income of the (number) _____ operators in the $500-up-to-$600 income bracket. Thus, the coordinates of the point on the frequency polygon are _____ and _____ operators.

$550
3

$550 and 3

13

The coordinates of the first plot of $550 and 3 frequencies (*f*) is shown. Fill in the blanks and draw the frequency polygon by plotting the remaining points. Then connect the points by straight lines. The usual practice is to extend the lines to the midpoints of the classes above and below the extremes ($450 and $1,250).

Monthly Income after Taxes	Midpoints	f
$ 500 up to $ 600	$550	3
600 up to 700	——	5
700 up to 800	——	10
800 up to 900	——	17
900 up to 1,000	——	8
1,000 up to 1,100	——	5
1,100 up to 1,200	——	2

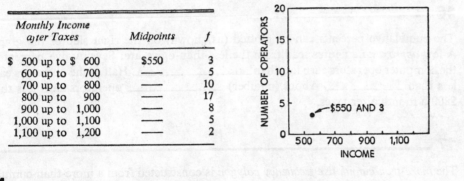

$550 AND 3

Midpoints are:
$650	$ 950
750	1,050
850	1,150

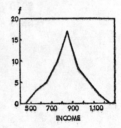

14

THE CUMULATIVE FREQUENCY

There are two cumulative frequency polygons (often called ogives). One is a *less-than-cumulative frequency polygon* and the other a *more-than-cumulative frequency polygon*.

The less-than-ogive is constructed from a less-than-cumulative frequency distribution. To design the cumulative frequency distribution, the frequencies are cumulated starting with the lowest income class and continuing through the highest income class. Now fill in the cumulative frequencies in the following table (extreme right column).

The upper limits of the income classes are also needed to construct the less-than-cumulative frequency polygon. (Insert the upper limits in the spaces provided.)

Monthly Income	Upper Limit of Class	Frequency in Class f	Number Receiving Less than Upper Limit of Class CF
$ 500 up to $ 600	$600	3	3
600 up to 700	700	5	8
700 up to 800	——	10	——
800 up to 900	——	17	——
900 up to 1,000	——	8	——
1,000 up to 1,100	——	5	——
1,100 up to 1,200	——	2	——
		50	

Upper Limits	Cumulative
$ 800	18
900	35
1,000	43
1,100	48
1,200	50

15

The upper limits of the income classes and the corresponding cumulative frequencies are plotted to construct the less-than-cumulative frequency polygon. The first plot in the adjacent exhibit indicates that 3 computer operators earn less than $600, the second plot that 8 earn less than $700, and so on. Complete the less-than-cumulative frequency polygon. Connect the points by straight lines. (Note: the usual practice is to extend the line to the X-axis as shown.)

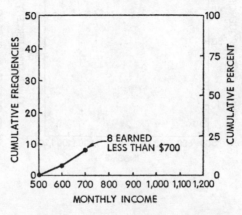

8 EARNED LESS THAN $700

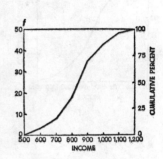

16 ───

The cumulative percents can be plotted (as shown) on the right side of the graph. A few *approximate* figures read from the less-than-ogive are: Seventy-five percent of the computer operators earn less than _____. Half of the operators earn less than _____. About (number) _____ operators earn less than $800 a month after taxes.

$930
$840
18

17 ───

The *more-than-cumulative frequency polygon* is constructed from a more-than-cumulative frequency distribution. Starting with the *highest* income class the frequencies are cumulated up to the lowest income class. The *lower limits* of each class are also needed to construct the more-than-ogive. Accumulate the frequencies and indicate the lower limits in the following distribution of operator incomes. Start with the highest income class.

Monthly Income	Lower Limit of Class	Frequencies *f*	Number of Operators Receiving More than Lower Limit of Class CF
$ 500 up to $ 600	$ ___	3	─
600 up to 700	___	5	─
700 up to 800	___	10	─
800 up to 900	___	17	─
900 up to 1,000	___	8	
1,000 up to 1,100	___	5	7
1,100 up to 1,200	1,100	2	2
		50	

Lower Limits	CF
$ 500	50
600	47
700	42
800	32
900	15
1,000	7
1,100	2

18 ───

A MORE-THAN-CUMULATIVE
FREQUENCY POLYGON

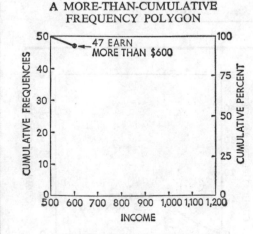

The lower limits of the income classes and the corresponding cumulative frequencies are plotted to construct the more-than-cumulative frequency polygon. The first plot in the adjacent exhibit indicates that all 50 operators earn more than $500, the second plot that 47 earn more than $600, and so forth. Complete the more-than-cumulative polygon. Connect the points by straight lines. Extend the line to the X-axis indicating that none of the operators earned $1,200 or more.

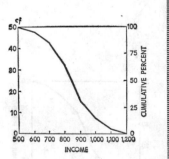

19

A few *approximate* figures read from the more-than-ogive are: None of the operators earn more than _____. 50 percent of them earn more than _____. About (number) _____ operators earn $750 or more. All of the operators earn _____ or more after taxes.

$1,200 $840

39

$500

Final Self-Review Examination

First, answer all of the questions. Then check your answers against those given at the end of this chapter. Scoring: 10 problems × 10 points each = 100 possible points.

20. The outside diameter of a shaft is measured by a special gauge. In order to organize the measurements, the following was designed.

Measurement

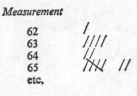

62
63
64
65
etc.

The data are considered (discrete/continuous) (a)_____. The ordered numbers 62, 63, 64, etc., are called an (b)_____, and the /XX/ / are (c)_____.

21. The measurements were then organized as follows:

Outside Diameter	Number of Measurements
62 up to 65	7
65 up to 68	17
68 up to 71	26
71 up to 74	14
74 up to 77	6

The previous table of outside diameters is known as a (a)_____. The data in the table is considered (grouped/ungrouped) (b)_____.

22. In the table of outside diameters (frame #21), the size of the class interval is (a)_____, and the numbers on the right (7, 17, etc.) are called (b)_____.

23. Present the data on outside diameters (frame #21) in the form of a *histogram* in the following left grid. Label axes and insert essential numbers.

24. Present the data on outside diameters (frame #21) in the form of a *frequency polygon* in the right grid. Label axes and insert essential numbers.

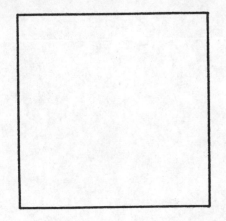

25. Using the same distribution of outside diameters (frame #21), portray the data in a *less-than-cumulative frequency polygon* (left).

26. Now on the right draw a *more-than-cumulative frequency polygon* using the same distribution (frame #21). Include essential numbers.

27. Based on any of the graphs, answer the following questions. The largest concentration of outside diameters are in the (a)_____ _____ up to _____ class. One-

fourth of the outside diameters measured less than (approximately) (b)_____

28. (Refer again to the graphs.) Approximately half of the outside diameters measured more than (a)_____. About (b)_____ _____ percent of the shafts measured more than 71 on the special gauge.

29. Briefly, indicate the purpose(s) of organizing data into a frequency distribution and drawing various graphs._____ _____ _____

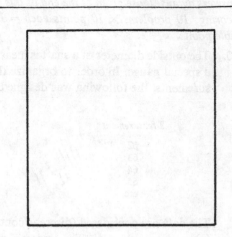

Answers to Final Self-Review Examination

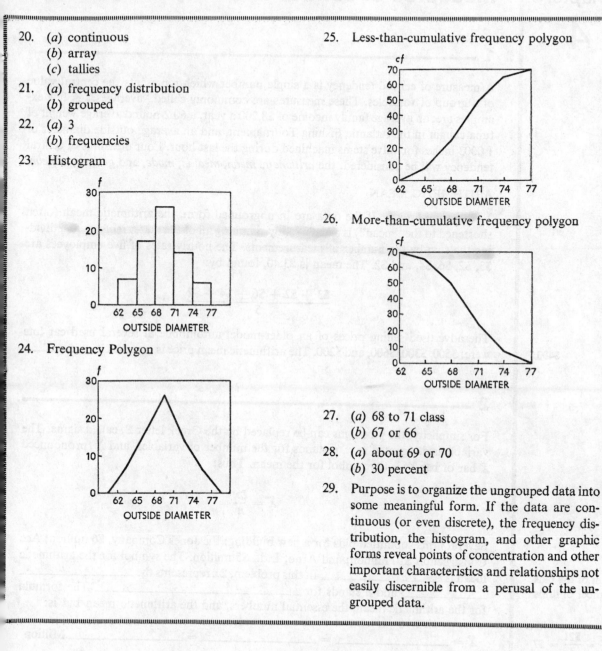

20. (a) continuous
    (b) array
    (c) tallies
21. (a) frequency distribution
    (b) grouped
22. (a) 3
    (b) frequencies
23. Histogram

24. Frequency Polygon

25. Less-than-cumulative frequency polygon

26. More-than-cumulative frequency polygon

27. (a) 68 to 71 class
    (b) 67 or 66
28. (a) about 69 or 70
    (b) 30 percent
29. Purpose is to organize the ungrouped data into some meaningful form. If the data are continuous (or even discrete), the frequency distribution, the histogram, and other graphic forms reveal points of concentration and other important characteristics and relationships not easily discernible from a perusal of the ungrouped data.

Measures of central tendency

1

A measure of central tendency is a single number which represents the central value of a group of variables. These measures are commonly called "averages." A few examples are: an average family income of $8,200 a year, a 60.2-pound average weight of tuna caught in the Atlantic Fishing Tournament, and an average outside diameter of 1.0003 inches for valve stems machined during the last hour. Four measures of central tendency will be considered: the *arithmetic mean, median, mode,* and *geometric mean.*

ARITHMETIC MEAN

Ungrouped data. If the data are in ungrouped form, the arithmetic mean (often shortened to the "mean") is calculated by summing all of the measurements and dividing the sum by the number of measurements. The hourly rates of five employees are $3, $2, $6, $4, and $2. The mean is $3.40, found by:

$$\frac{\$3 + \$2 + \$6 + \$4 + \$2}{5}$$

$400

The advertised selling prices of an older-model automobile at several used car lots were: $500, $300, $600, and $200. The arithmetic mean price is _____

2

For simplicity, the plus signs can be replaced by the Greek letter Σ, called sigma. The variable is designated as x, n stands for the number of variables, and $\bar{X}$ (pronounced X bar or bar X) is the symbol for the mean. Thus:

$$\bar{X} = \frac{\Sigma x}{n}$$

$\bar{X}$ sum of the bids
number of firms

Several firms submitted bids for a new building: the Jones Company, $6 million; Ace Construction $10 million; and Arno, Ltd., $5 million. The symbol for the arithmetic mean is _____. In this problem, Σx represents the _____ _____, and n stands for _____. The formula for the arithmetic mean, the essential numbers, and the arithmetic mean bid is:

$\frac{\Sigma x}{n} = \frac{\$21}{3} = \$7$

$$\bar{X} = \underline{\hspace{2cm}} = \underline{\hspace{2cm}} = \underline{\hspace{2cm}} \text{ Million}$$

3

If n and $\bar{X}$ are known, Σx can be found. For example, the mean wage for the 30 employees of the Betz Stamping Plant for the week of July 1 was $120. The total employee

$3,600

payroll for the week was _____.

4

Grouped data. The tensile strengths of several wires (in pounds per square inch) are 6, 6, 7, 7, 7, 8, 8, and 9.4 pounds. The tensile strengths were grouped into a frequency distribution.

The midpoint of each class is used to represent the class. The midpoint of the class (designated as x) is then multiplied times the number of frequencies in that class. The sum of these products is divided by the total number of frequencies to give the arithmetic mean. In terms of a formula:

$$\bar{X} = \frac{\Sigma fx}{n} \quad \text{or} \quad \frac{\Sigma fx}{\Sigma f}$$

Insert the missing numbers:

Tensile Strengths (Pounds per Square Inch)	Number of Wires f	Midpoint of Class x	fx
5.50 up to 6.50	2	6	12
6.50 up to 7.50	3	7	21
7.50 up to 8.50	2	8	16
8.50 up to 9.50	1	9	9
	8	Total	58

x	fx
	21
8	16
9	9
	58

5

The formula for the mean of grouped data, the essential numbers and the mean tensile strength are:

$$\bar{X} = \underline{\hspace{2cm}} = \underline{\hspace{2cm}} = \underline{\hspace{2cm}} \text{ pounds per square inch.}$$

$$\frac{\Sigma fx}{\Sigma f} = \frac{58}{8} = 7.25$$

6

The mean of the original ungrouped data (6, 6, 7, 7, 7, 8, 8, and 9.4) is _____ pounds. Note that the mean of the grouped data (7.25) and the mean of the ungrouped data (7.3) are not identical. The difference is due to the loss of accuracy when the data were grouped. The mean would probably be another value if a different class interval had been selected.

7.3

7

The annual sales of selected firms were organized as follows.

Annual Sales (In Millions)	Number of Firms
$ 5 up to $15	3
15 up to 25	5
25 up to 35	6
35 up to 45	4
45 up to 55	2

$$\bar{X} = \frac{\Sigma fx}{\Sigma f}$$
$$= \frac{\$570}{20}$$

The arithmetic mean annual sales is $_____ . _____ million.

$$= \$28.5$$

8 _____

MEDIAN

Ungrouped data. The median is the value of a point on a scale above which half of the values are found and below which the other half of the values lie. To determine the median of ungrouped data, the values are first arranged from low to high. Arrange the incomes of five individuals in ascending order. The incomes are: $5,000, $4,900, $6,000, $5,500, and $100,000.

$ 5,000	$4,900
$ 5,500	$_____
$ 6,000	$_____
$100,000	$_____
	$_____

$5,500   median

The middle income is _____. This income is called the _____.

9 _____

The median income of $5,500 seems to be a typical income since all but one individual are in the $4,000-up-to-$6,000 income range. The median is a more representative measure of central tendency than is the arithmetic mean which is _____.

$24,280

Thus, the median is usually a more appropriate measure if one or more extremely

high

_____ (or low) observations are included. What would the median

same $5,500

income be if the highest income were $1 million instead of $100,000? _____

same $5,500

_____. Had the lowest income been $2,000 instead of $4,900, the median income would be _____.

10 _____

If there is an even number of ungrouped observations, the median is halfway between the two center observations. A sample of prices of Grade D pine lumber at four lumber yards revealed prices of $0.28, $0.32, $0.22, and $0.21. To determine the median price,

arranged from low to high

the prices must first be _____. The median price is

$0.25

_____. (Note that no lumber yard had a price of exactly $0.25.)

11 _____

Grouped data. There is a minimal amount of work involved in arranging a few ungrouped observations from low to high and selecting the middle value. A large number of observations, however, presents a problem of ordering the data and finding the middle item. Instead, the quantitative data may be tallied directly into classes and the median approximated from the resulting frequency distribution. Also, in many cases the original data from which the frequency distribution was designed are not available and the median must be estimated from the grouped data.

The 60 junior executives in a firm were rated by top management on a scale from 50 up to 100. The composite ratings were then organized into a frequency distribution for further study.

Ratings of Junior Executives	Number f	Cumulative Number CF_i
50 up to 60............................	9	9
60 up to 70............................	15	24
70 up to 80............................	20	44
80 up to 90............................	11	55
90 up to 100...........................	5	60
Total........................	60	

The problem involves estimating the composite rating of the junior executive in the middle of the distribution. He is the _____th junior executive counting down from the lowest rated.

30

12 ────────────────────────────────

The position of the 30th junior executive is shown schematically as follows.

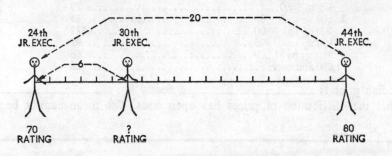

Interpolating, the rating earned by the 30th junior executive is _____/20 of the distance between a rating of 70 and _____. This amount (6/20 of 10, or _____) is added to 70. Thus, the median rating of the junior executives is _____ _____.

6
80
3
73

13 ────────────────────────────────

One assumption when interpolating the median is that the ratings are evenly distributed between 70 and 80. If the ungrouped data were available, the median rating might not be exactly 73. Thus, it probably should be said that *about* half of the junior executives had a rating less than _____ and *about* half more than _____ _____.

73
73

14 ────────────────────────────────

The median may also be computed using the formula:

$$\text{Median} = L_2 + \frac{\frac{n}{2} - CF_2}{f}\,(i)$$

where: L_2 is the lower limit of the class in which the median falls. The 30th junior executive accumulated from the lowest rating is found in the _____ up to _____

70 up to 80

70
60
24

20
10

$$L_2 + \frac{\frac{n}{2} - CF_2}{f}(i)$$

$$= 70 + \frac{\frac{60}{2} - 24}{20}(10) = 73$$

_____ class and _____ is the lower limit of that class. n is the total number of junior executives, or _____ (number). CF_2 is the cumulative frequency for the class immediately below the median class. There are _____ (number) junior executives accumulated below the median class. The frequency (f) in the median class is _____ (number). The letter i stands for the width of the class interval of the median class. The width in this problem is _____. Thus, the formula for the median, essential numbers, and the answer:

Median = _____   =   _____   = _____ (answer)

Note that the answer is the same as found previously (frame #12).

15 ────────────────────────────────

The prices paid for a three-piece livingroom suite were tabulated by the assistant buyer into the following frequency distribution.

Price Paid for Suite	Number of Sales
Up to $600	20
$ 600 up to $ 700	83
700 up to 800	122
800 up to 900	91
900 up to 1,000	66
1,000 and over	18

$779.51,
$700 + 97/122 of $100

The median price is _____, found by: _____.
Note that the distribution of prices has open ends. The mean cannot be found.

16 ────────────────────────────────

MODE

Ungrouped data. The *mode* is defined as the value of the observation which appears most frequently. If there is only one mode, the distribution is called *unimodal*. If there are two values which appear most frequently, the distribution is called *bimodal*. The ages of a group of draftees are: 19, 21, 20, 21, 20, 21, 21, and 24 years. The data are (grouped/ungrouped) _____ and the distribution is (unimodal/bimodal) _____. The mode is _____. Hourly production of individuals making identical assemblies are 5, 8, 8, 7, 9, 10, 10, 8, 10, and 11 units. The distribution is (unimodal/bimodal) _____. The modes are _____ and _____.

ungrouped
unimodal   21 years

bimodal
8 units, 10 units

17 ────────────────────────────────

Grouped data. The *crude* or *observed* mode for data grouped into a frequency distribution is the midpoint of the class in which the greatest number of frequencies are found. The observed mode for the distribution in frame 15 is _____.

$750

18 ────────────────────────────────

GEOMETRIC MEAN

The geometric mean is defined as the nth root of the product of n numbers. The formula is:

$$\text{Geometric mean} = \sqrt[n]{(x_1)\,(x_2)\,(x_3)\ldots(x_n)}$$

One important business application is determining the average percent increase in sales, production, or other variable over a period of time. A modification of the formula is:

$$\text{Geometric mean} = \sqrt[n-1]{\frac{\text{Value for the last period of time}}{\text{Value for the first period of time}}} - 1$$

For example, sales for 1969 were $180 million, and for 1963 they were $100 million. What is the average annual percent increase in sales from 1963 through 1969. Note there are seven years.

$$\text{Geometric mean} = \sqrt[7-1]{\frac{\$180}{\$100}} - 1 = \sqrt[6]{1.80} - 1$$

Using logarithms to find the 6th root of 1.80:

$$\frac{\log \text{ of } 1.80}{6} = \frac{0.2553}{6} = 0.0426$$

The antilog of 0.0426 is approximately 1.103. Then 1.103 − 1 = 0.103. Sales increased 10.3 percent per year on the average from 1963 to 1969.

Similarly, the approximate average (geometric mean) annual percent increase of a stock which rose from $20 in 1961 to $117 in 1969 is _____ percent (nearest whole percent).

about 25 percent

19

RELATIONSHIP OF THE MEAN, MEDIAN AND MODE

If a frequency distribution is bell-shaped (symmetrical), the mean, median, and mode are equal. (See the following exhibit.) However, if the frequency distribution is not symmetrical (called asymmetrical, or skewed) the relationship among the averages changes. The graph on the right portrays a *positively skewed* distribution. Suppose that it represents the distribution of family incomes contiguous to a proposed shopping center. The arithmetic mean is the highest of the three averages, the median is the next largest, and the mode the smallest. The mean income is the highest because it is being influenced by a few extremely high incomes.

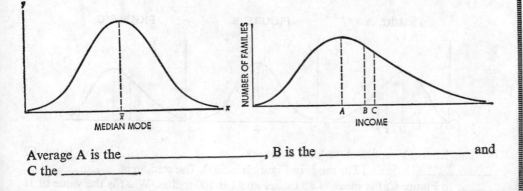

A SYMMETRICAL DISTRIBUTION   A POSITIVE SKEWED DISTRIBUTION

Average A is the _____, B is the _____ and C the _____.

Mode   Median
Mean

20 ———————————————————————————————

If the distribution is only moderately skewed, one average can be approximated if the other two are known by either:

$$\text{Mode} = \text{mean} - 3(\text{mean} - \text{median})$$
$$\text{Median} = \frac{2(\text{mean}) + \text{mode}}{3}$$
$$\text{Mean} = \frac{3(\text{median}) - \text{mode}}{2}$$

$12,000

If the modal family income were $9,000 and the median $11,000, the approximate mean income is _____. (Note that the median is about two thirds of the distance between the mode and the mean.)

If the ages of a group were organized into a frequency distribution and the mean age computed to be 60 years and the mode 30 years, the median age is approximately

50 years

_____ years.

21 ———————————————————————————————

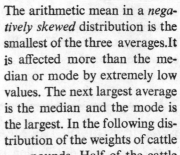

The arithmetic mean in a *negatively skewed* distribution is the smallest of the three averages. It is affected more than the median or mode by extremely low values. The next largest average is the median and the mode is the largest. In the following distribution of the weights of cattle

600
400 600
negatively

sold at the stockyards, the mode is about _____ pounds. Half of the cattle weighed less than _____ pounds. More cattle weighed _____ pounds than any other weight. The distribution is _____ skewed.

22 ———————————————————————————————

positively skewed
bell-shaped or symmetrical
negatively skewed

In review, describe the shape of the distribution in Figure A _____ _____, in Figure B _____, and Figure C _____.

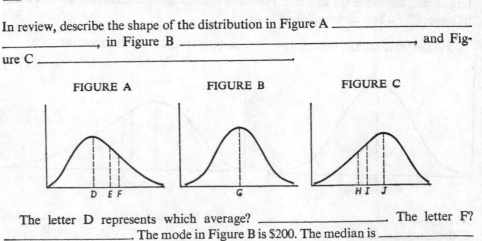

FIGURE A   FIGURE B   FIGURE C

mode
mean
also $200

The letter D represents which average? _____. The letter F? _____. The mode in Figure B is $200. The median is _____. In Figure C, the mean is 80 inches and I is 100 inches. What is the value of J?

_____ inches. In Figure C, half of the values are over _____   140 100
inches.

23 _____

SUMMARY OF THE CHARACTERISTICS OF MEASURES OF CENTRAL TENDENCY

The arithmetic mean is the most commonly used average. All the values are needed for its computation. If all of the values are clustered near the mean, and if the distribution is somewhat symmetrical, the mean can be considered a representative average. Extremely high (or low) values unduly affect it, and an unrepresentative average may result. Generally speaking, if the distribution of values is skewed, the (average) _____ is considered a poor average to use to represent the   arithmetic mean
group.

The median, however, is not affected by extreme values and better represents the group of values when the distribution is skewed. Also, the median can be computed if the distribution has open ends. The arithmetic mean cannot be determined for an open-end frequency distribution because _____   midpoints (X) are
_____.   not available

The mode is not used as often as the mean or median but is a very appropriate average to use if one value near the center of the distribution appears quite frequently. If the distribution is symmetrical or slightly skewed the mode (can/cannot) _____   can
be determined. Also, the mode (can/cannot) _____ be computed if the distribution has open ends.   can

The geometric mean is infrequently used partly because logarithms are needed for its computation. It is the only average, however, that gives the correct answer in problems involving _____.   average annual percent
increase

Final Self-Review Examination

First, answer all of the questions. Then check your answers against those given at the end of this chapter. Scoring: 10 problems × 10 points each = 100 possible points.

24. The ages of several typists are 22, 26, 29, 23, and 18 years. The median age is (a)_____ years. The arithmetic mean age is (b)_____ years.

    Questions 25 through 28 are based on the following frequency distribution.

Hourly Wages of Workers	Number of Workers
$ 2 up to $ 4	1
4 up to 6	3
6 up to 8	20
8 up to 10	4
10 up to 12	2

25. The arithmetic mean hourly wage is _____ _____ (nearest cent).

26. The median hourly wage is _____ _____ (nearest cent).

27. The observed mode is _____ _____.

28. Based on the three measures of central tendency, the distribution of wages can be considered (positively skewed/negatively skewed/symmetrical) _____.

29. If a frequency distribution is only slightly skewed, *but has open ends*, which of the following measure, or measures, of central tendency *cannot* be computed? (arithmetic mean/ median/mode) _____
_____

30. The production of a small plant increased from 40 units in 1964 to 74 units in 1969. The average annual percent increase in production is _____ percent. (Note: nearest whole percent. It is not necessary to interpolate.)

31. Most of the prices paid for 120 antique silver pieces at an auction varied between $5 and $12 except for one rare piece which brought $71,-000. Which of the three most commonly used averages (arithmetic mean/median/mode) would not be a representative average to use? _____.

32. The following frequency polygon portrays a distribution of tensile strengths of copper wire. The letter A represents an average called the (a)_____ and the letter B represents the (b)_____

_____ tensile strength. Is the distribution (symmetrical/positive skewed/negative skewed)?(c) _____.

DISTRIBUTION OF TENSILE STRENGTHS

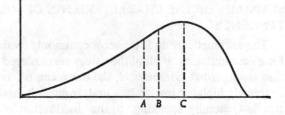

33. It was found that a distribution of incomes in a suburb was moderately skewed. The mean income was computed to be $15,000 and the median income $14,000. The approximate modal (mode) income is _____

Answers to Final Self-Review Examination

24. (a) 23,   (b) 23.6 years
25. $7.20, found by $216/30
26. $7.10, found by $6 + 11/20 of $2
27. $7.00
28. positively skewed
29. arithmetic mean

30. about 13 percent
31. arithmetic mean
32. (a) arithmetic mean
    (b) median
    (c) negatively skewed
33. $12,000

Measures of dispersion and skewness

1 ————————————————————————————————

The basic concept of *dispersion*, alternatively called *variation* or *spread*, can be illustrated by analyzing the weekly incomes of two groups of employees; namely, the production employees and the office employees.

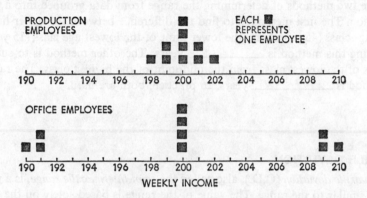

The arithmetic mean weekly income of both groups is _____. Any comparison of the income structure of the two groups based only on the average, however, would be misleading. This is so because the incomes of the _____ employees are spread out more than the incomes of the _____ employees. Thus, additional statistical measures to describe the dispersion, also called _____ ____ or _____, are needed. Five measures of absolute dispersion are studied. They are the *range*, the *quartile deviation*, the *average deviation*, the *variance*, and the *standard deviation*.

$200

office
production
variation or
spread

2 ————————————————————————————————

MEASURES OF ABSOLUTE DISPERSION: RANGE

Ungrouped data. The lowest paid employee in the office (frame #1) earned $190 a week and the highest, $210. The difference of $20 is called the *range*. The range of the weekly incomes for the production group is _____.

$4, found
  by $202 − $198

3 ————————————————————————————————

There is more spread in the incomes of the office employees than in the incomes of the production employees because the range of _____ is greater than _____.
The range of $4 for the production employees compared with the range of $20 for the office employees indicates that the incomes of the production employees tend to cluster more about the mean. It also indicates that the mean income of _____ for the production employees is a (more/less) _____ representative average than the $200 mean income of the office employees.

$20 $4

$200
more

31

4 ──

Grouped data. The same concept is used if the data are grouped into a frequency distribution. Suppose the ages of the office employees were grouped as follows.

Ages	Number of Office Workers
15 up to 25 years	12
25 up to 35 years	51
35 up to 45 years	16

There are two methods of determining the range from data grouped into a frequency distribution. The first method is to find the difference between the upper limit of the highest age class (45 years) and the lower limit of the lowest age class (15 years). The range using this method is _____ years. The other method is to subtract the midpoint of the lowest class from the midpoint of the highest class. The range using this method is _____ years. In practice, both are used.

30

20

5 ──

QUARTILE DEVIATION

The *quartile deviation* (Q.D.), also called the *semi-interquartile range*, is a positional measure similar to the range. The value of the range is based solely on the difference between the _____ and _____ observations. The quartile deviation is based on the difference between the first quartile (Q_1) and the third quartile (Q_3). The first quartile is the value corresponding to the point below which 25 percent of the observations lie. The third quartile is the value corresponding to the point above which 25 percent of the observations lie. Thus, between Q_1 and Q_3 can be found the middle _____ percent of the observations.

lowest and highest

50

6 ──

The concept of the first quartile (Q_1) is illustrated by considering the tensile strengths of 60 wires. Its computation is very similar to the median (Q_2) studied in the previous chapter.

Tensile Strengths (Pounds per Square Inch)	Number of Wires f	Cumulative Frequencies CF
600 up to 700	3	3
700 up to 800	6	9
800 up to 900	13	22
900 up to 1,000	20	42
1,000 up to 1,100	10	52
1,100 up to 1,200	8	60
	60	

There are 60 wires. Counting up from the lowest class to include the first quarter of the observations (15)—found by dividing 60 by 4—the point located is called the first quartile. The tensile strength on the scale below which are located the tensile strengths of 15 wires can be interpolated as follows: Counting into the distribution there are 9 wires accumulated up to 800 pounds and 22 wires accumulated up to 900 pounds. Logically, the first quartile is between 800 and 900 pounds. The tensile strength below which are one fourth of the wires is 6/13 the way up from 800 pounds.

$$Q_1 = 800 + \frac{6}{13} \text{ of } 100 = 846.15 \text{ pounds (846 rounded)}$$

Shown schematically:

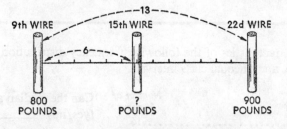

Using this method of interpolation, determine the third quartile, Q_3 = _____ _____.

1,030 pounds, found by 1,000 + 3/10 of 100

7 ————————————————————

Half the distance between the third quartile and the first quartile is *semi-interquartile range*, or the *quartile deviation* (Q.D.). Design a formula, insert the appropriate data, and determine the quartile deviation.

Q.D. = _____   =   _____.

$$\text{Q.D.} = \frac{Q_3 - Q_1}{2}$$
$$= \frac{1,030 - 846}{2}$$
$$= 92 \text{ pounds}$$

8 ————————————————————

If the distribution is symmetrical, the distance between Q_1 and Q_2 (the median) is equal to the distance between _____ and _____. This concept is portrayed in the following distribution representing the annual incomes of middle management.

Q_2 and Q_3

The median is _____. The quartile deviation is _____. If the quartile deviation is subtracted from, and added to, the median, the resulting answers are _____ and _____ respectively. These two amounts are the _____ and _____ quartiles. This relationship between the median and the (measure of dispersion) _____ is only true if the distribution is _____.

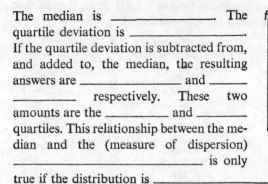

$40,000
$10,000

$30,000 and $50,000

first and third

quartile deviation

symmetrical or bell-shaped

9 ————————————————————

If the frequency distribution is skewed *positively*, the distance between Q_1 and Q_2 will be less than the distance between Q_2 and Q_3. For the following _____

positively

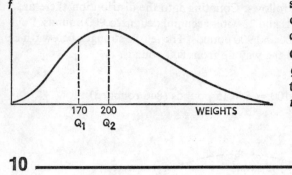

any guess over 230 pounds

skewed distribution of the weights of football players, guess the third quartile. _____.

Conversely, the distance between Q_1 and Q_2 is larger than the distance between Q_2 and Q_3 in a *negatively* skewed distribution.

10

Two unusual characteristics of the following frequency distribution are an open-end (under 20 years), and unequal class intervals.

Ages of Visitors	Number of Visitors
Under 20 years	16
20 up to 30 years	32
30 up to 40 years	83
40 up to 60 years	29
60 up to 90 years	10

yes

yes   yes

yes

no (because of the open end)

Can the median age be computed? (yes/no) _____, Q_1 ?

_____, Q_3?

Q.D. ? _____. The range?
_____

11

AVERAGE DEVIATION

Ungrouped data. The *average deviation* is also called the *mean deviation*. As the name implies, it is computed by averaging the deviations from the mean, or median, disregarding the algebraic signs. The sign $\|$ signifies that plus and minus signs are to be ignored. The formula is:

$$\text{A.D.} = \frac{\Sigma|X - \bar{X}|}{n} \quad \text{or} \quad \frac{\Sigma|X - \text{median}|}{n}$$

The weekly incomes of the production employees from frame #1 are used to illustrate the computation of the average deviation. The mean income is $200. First, the absolute difference between each income and the mean income was found.

Then:

$$\text{A.D.} = \frac{\Sigma|X - \bar{X}|}{n}$$

$$= \frac{\$8}{10}$$

$$= \$0.80$$

Weekly Income of Production Employees	
X	$X - \bar{X}$
$198	$-$2
199	$-$ 1
199	$-$ 1
200	0
200	0
200	0
200	0
201	$+$ 1
201	$+$ 1
202	$+$ 2
	$\overline{\$8}$

Now compute the average deviation for the incomes of the office employees from frame #1; namely, $190, $200, $200, $209, $191, $200, $210, $200, $191, and $209. The average deviation is _____.

$5.60, found by $56/10

12

A comparison of the two average deviations indicates that there is less dispersion in the incomes of the _____ workers because _____ is less than _____. Also, the average income of the production employees is more representative than the average income of the office employees because _____

_____

production $0.80
$5.60
$0.80 is less than $5.60

The average deviation of grouped data is seldom encountered.

13

VARIANCE AND THE STANDARD DEVIATION

Ungrouped data. The *variance* is also based on the deviations from the mean. To find the variance (s^2) of the income figures for the production employees, the deviations from the mean ($X - \bar{X}$) are squared ($X - \bar{X}$)^2, then summed $\Sigma(X - \bar{X})^2$ and averaged by dividing by the number of men or n. The formula, essential work, and the answer for the variance follows.

Income X	Income − Mean $X - \bar{X}$	$(X - \bar{X})^2$
$198	−$2	$ 4
199	− 1	1
199	− 1	1
200	0	0
200	0	0
200	0	0
200	0	0
201	+ 1	1
201	+ 1	1
202	+ 2	4
		12

$$s^2 = \frac{\Sigma(X - \bar{X})^2}{n}$$
$$= \frac{\$12}{10}$$
$$= \$1.20$$

Now compute the variance for the incomes of office workers; namely, $190, $200, $200, $209, $191, $200, $210, $200, $191, and $209. The variance is _____
_____

$52.40, found by $524/10

14

Again, a comparison of the two measures of dispersion (a variance of $52.40 for the office employees and $1.20 for the production employees), indicates that there is less dispersion in the incomes of the _____ employees because $1.20 is less than $52.40. Also, the average income for the production employees is more representative for the same reason, i.e., _____ is less than _____.

production

$1.20 $52.40

15

The variance is difficult to interpret. In this problem, the unit of variance is (dollars)^2. To convert this vague concept to dollars, the square root of the variance is computed. The square root of the variance (s^2) is the *standard deviation*, or (s).

The variance of the incomes of the production employees was found to be $1.20. The square root of the variance, called the _____ _____ is approximately $1.10. (See Appendix Table III for square roots.)

standard deviation

$7.24
production

The variance of the incomes of the office employees was computed to be $52.40. The standard deviation is $_____. Again a comparison of the two standard deviations indicates that there is less dispersion in the incomes of the _____ employees.

16 ————————————————————————

Grouped data. To illustrate the computation of the standard deviation for grouped data consider the following wages of welders. First, the midpoint (X) of each wage class is found. Then each X is squared (X^2) and multiplied by the appropriate number of frequencies in the class to give fX^2. In terms of a formula, the standard deviation for grouped data is:

$$s = \sqrt{\frac{\Sigma fX^2}{n} - \bar{X}^2} \quad \text{or} \quad \sqrt{\frac{\Sigma fX^2}{n} - \left(\frac{\Sigma fX}{n}\right)^2}$$

Complete the following table.

Hourly Wages of Welders	Number of Men f	Midpoint X	X²	fX²	fX
$3 up to $5........	2	$4	$16	$32	$8
5 up to 7........	5	——	——	——	——
7 up to 9........	3	——	——	——	——
Total........	—			——	——

Give the formula for the standard deviation, insert figures from the table, and find the standard deviation.

$s =$ _____ = _____ = _____ (answer)

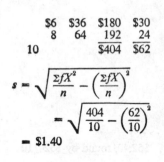

$6 $36 $180 $30
 8   64   192   24
10          $404 $62

$$s = \sqrt{\frac{\Sigma fX^2}{n} - \left(\frac{\Sigma fX}{n}\right)^2}$$
$$= \sqrt{\frac{404}{10} - \left(\frac{62}{10}\right)^2}$$
$$= \$1.40$$

17 ————————————————————————

Now that the standard deviation has been computed to be $1.40, how is it interpreted? Unfortunately, it cannot be as easily defined as the range or median. However, the standard deviation can be considered a unit of measurement similar to the ton, foot, or pounds per square inch tensile strength. The standard deviations from two distributions can be used as a common denominator to compare the dispersion of two distributions and the representativeness of the two means. Assuming that the two means are approximately equal, standard deviations of $1.40 for the welders and $1 for a distribution of the wages of diemakers indicates that the mean of the (welders/diemakers) _____ is more representative and that there is less dispersion in the wages of the (welders/diemakers) _____.

diemakers
diemakers

18 ————————————————————————

Another use of the standard deviation as a tool of analysis is in its relationship to the mean of a *normal distribution*. (It is sufficient at this point to indicate that the normal curve is often referred to as the Gaussian distribution after Karl Gauss. It is symmetrical and smoothed. Theoretically, the tails of the curve move off to infinity.) One relationship is in terms of the percent of the observations within one standard deviation below the mean and one standard deviation above the mean. In a normal distribution, exactly 68.3 percent of the values lie within plus and minus one standard deviation of the mean. (See the graph.)

THE AREAS UNDER THE NORMAL CURVE

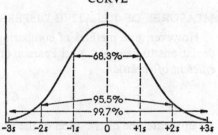

Further, the mean ($\bar{X}$) plus and minus (written $\pm$) two times the standard deviation includes approximately 95 percent of the observations. The $\bar{X} \pm 3(s)$ includes about 99.7 percent of the observations.

The quality control department of a tire manufacturer tested the durability of a proposed new tire by taking a large sample of the tires and running them on a test machine until each disintegrated. The mileage of each at the time of the blow-out was organized into a frequency distribution. The mean mileage of the tires was 40,000 miles, the standard deviation 2,000 miles.

Reading from the following graph:

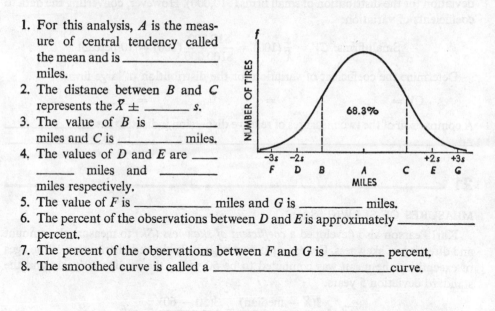

1. For this analysis, A is the measure of central tendency called the mean and is _____ miles.

2. The distance between B and C represents the $\bar{X} \pm$ _____ s.

3. The value of B is _____ miles and C is _____ miles.

4. The values of D and E are _____ _____ miles and _____ miles respectively.

5. The value of F is _____ miles and G is _____ miles.

6. The percent of the observations between D and E is approximately _____ percent.

7. The percent of the observations between F and G is _____ percent.

8. The smoothed curve is called a _____ curve.

1. 40,000

2. 1

3. 38,000
   42,000

4. 36,000   44,000

5. 34,000   46,000

6. 95

7. 99.7

8. normal, bell-shaped, or symmetrical

19

In the previous discussion, a *direct* and meaningful comparison of two standard deviations (or other measures of dispersion) could be made because the means were approximately equal. Frequently, however, the means are quite far apart or two dissimilar groups must be compared. A direct comparison of the standard deviations would be meaningless. For example, a meaningful comparison of the incomes of the presidents of the top 100 firms in the United States and the incomes of migrant workers (could/could not) _____ be made using means and standard deviations. Similarly, the distribution of the incomes of the presidents and a distribution of their ages are (similar/dissimilar) _____ and (should/should not) _____ _____ be compared *directly*.

could not

dissimilar

should not

20 ───

MEASURES OF RELATIVE DISPERSION

However, one method of comparing two distributions is to convert the standard deviations to percents. Karl Pearson (1857–1936) originated a measure called the *coefficient of variation.*

$$CV = \frac{s}{\bar{X}}(100)$$

To illustrate, the distribution of the profits of a selected group of small firms and the profit of a selected group of large firms are to be compared. Both distributions are somewhat normally distributed.

Small Firms	Large Firms
$\bar{X} = \$100,000$	$\bar{X} = \$2,000,000$
$s = \$ \ 10,000$	$s = \$ \ 200,000$

There is a tendency to conclude that there is more dispersion in the distribution of the large firms because the standard deviation of $200,000 is greater than the standard deviation for the distribution of small firms ($10,000). However, converting the data to coefficients of variation:

$$\text{Small firms: } CV = \frac{s}{\bar{X}}(100) = \frac{\$10,000}{\$100,000}(100) = 10 \text{ percent}$$

Determine the coefficient of variation for the distribution of large firms.

$$CV = \qquad = \qquad = \underline{\qquad}.$$

A comparison of the two measures of relative dispersion indicates that _____
_____

21 ───

MEASURES OF SKEWNESS

Karl Pearson also developed a *coefficient of skewness (Sk)* to measure the amount and direction of skewness. For example, in a negatively skewed distribution of the ages of executives, the mean was computed to be 50 years, the median 60 years and the standard deviation 5 years.

$$Sk = \frac{3(\bar{X} - \text{median})}{s} = \frac{3(50 - 60)}{5} = -6$$

The coefficient of skewness for a comparative group of teachers was found to be −9.3. The skewness for the group of teachers is also negative and a comparison of the two groups indicates that the distribution of the ages of teachers is more highly skewed.

Computations for distributions of the outside diameters of a shaft were: mean outside diameter 1.00025, median 1.00020, standard deviation 0.00010. The coefficient of skewness is _____.

If $Sk = 0.00$, what would it indicate? _____
_____

Left margin answers:

10 percent, found by [$200,000/$2,000,000] (100)
The relative dispersions of the two distributions are equal

+1.5, found by [3(1.00025 − 1.00020)]/0.00010
no skewness, or a symmetrical (normal) distribution

Final Self-Review Examination

First, answer all of the questions. Then check your answers against those given at the end of this chapter. Scoring: 10 problems × 10 points each = 100 possible points.

Questions 22 through 25 are based on the following sample of hourly wages: $3, $7, $2, and $8.

22. The range is $_____.

23. The average deviation is $_____.

24. The variance is $_____.

25. The standard deviation is $_____.

Questions 26 through 28 are based on the following distribution of amounts allocated by firms for capital improvements.

Amounts Allocated for Capital Improvements (In Millions)	Number of Firms
$1 up to $ 3	4
3 up to 5	7
5 up to 7	10
7 up to 9	6
9 up to 11	3
Total	30

26. The range is $_____ millions.

27. The quartile deviation is $_____ millions.

28. The variance is $_____ millions and the standard deviation is $_____ millions.

Questions 29 through 31 are based on the following production figures for three groups of workers. The three groups are identified by the name of the supervisor. The production figures were recorded over a long period of time and represent weekly production.

Measure	Supervisor		
	Jarnow	Arn	Smith
Arithmetic mean	800	780	820
Median	800	790	810
Mode	800	810	790
Standard deviation	20	40	60
Average deviation	16	32	48
Quartile deviation	14	28	40

29. The production of which group is the most erratic? (a)_____. The distribution of which group is negatively skewed? (b)_____.

30. The middle one half of the weeks, Supervisor Jarnow's group produced between (a)_____ and _____ units. The middle 95 percent of the weeks, Supervisor Jarnow's group produced between (b)_____ and _____ units.

31. The coefficient of variation for the production distribution of Supervisor Jarnow's group is (a)_____. The coefficient of skewness for the production distribution of Supervisor Smith's group is (b)_____.

Answers to Final Self-Review Examination

22. $6

23. $10/4 = $2.50

24. $26/4 = $6.50

25. square root of $6.50 = $2.55

26. either $10 or $8

27. $Q_1 = \$3 + 3.5/7$ of $2 = $4

    $Q_3 = \$7 + 1.5/6$ of $2 = $7.50

    Then Q.D. = $\dfrac{\$7.50 - \$4}{2} = \$1.75$

28. Variance = $\dfrac{\$1,172}{30} - \left(\dfrac{\$174}{30}\right)^2 = \$5.43$

    Standard deviation = $\sqrt{\$5.43} = \$2.33$

29. (a) Smith's group because distribution has largest measures of dispersion.

    (b) Arn's group

30. (a) 786 and 814 units

    (b) 760 and 840 units

31. (a) 20/800 (100) = 2.5 percent

    (b) 3(820 − 810)/60 = 0.5

chapter

6

A survey of probability concepts

1 ——

Methods of descriptive statistics were examined in the first five chapters. These methods dealt mainly with data collection (questionnaires and library sources), organization and presentation of data (frequency distributions, tables, and graphs), and data analysis (measures of central tendency and dispersion). Descriptive measures merely describe the business phenomena, such as the trend of sales the past 20 years, and an average annual increase of 3.4 percent. The businessman using these basic techniques of description does not take any risk of making an error, such as maintaining a too high level of inventory, or building a new plant and then finding it was not needed. (The only "error" he might make is entering a wrong number in the calculator or plotting data incorrectly on a graph.)

A second facet of statistics is called inductive statistics or statistical inference. It deals with inferences about the population based on incomplete (sample) data. To put it another way, inductive statistics are concerned with reasoning from the partial to the general. And, because only partial information is available, there is a risk of making an error. For example, the Roper, Gallup, and Harris opinion-gathering polls use sample data almost exclusively to predict the outcome of an election. Based on a relatively small group of potential voters, there is always the risk of an incorrect prediction (such as in 1948 when Thomas Dewey was favored to win). The level of inventory to maintain, and the strategy to be followed in marketing a new product, are but two business decision problems with the built-in danger of making an error. Seldom, if ever, does the decision maker have complete information on which to make a decision. If he is trying to determine how many television sets to make during the forthcoming year, the potential consumer demand for each model, possible changes in the price of raw materials, and the possible effect of a recently announced increase in a competitors warranty to seven years are but a few factors which must be assessed. Obviously, it would be impossible to study all relevant factors which might affect the decision on the number of each model to be produced during the year. Therefore, most business decisions

uncertainty   are made under conditions of (certainty/uncertainty) _____

risk   _____ and there is (no risk/risk) _____ involved.

2 ——

Thus, under conditions of uncertainty it is assumed that there is a risk involved regardless of the level of inventory, or production, decided upon. Probability theory has often been referred to as the science of uncertainty. The use of probability theory allows the decision maker with only limited information available to him to analyze the risks and minimize the gamble inherent in establishing the inventory at level A, level B, or level C. Thus, a knowledge of the concepts of probability is essential before discussing sampling (Chapters 8 and 9), tests of hypotheses (Chapter 10), decision making (Chapter 11), and Bayesian statistics (Chapter 12).

INTERPRETATIONS OF PROBABILITY

The *objective* interpretation of probability has been the dominant one in statistics until recent years. There is concern with events which can be repeated over and over under the same conditions. To illustrate, a balanced coin can be tossed into the air many times and the number of heads and tails recorded. A head will appear face up in about half of the tosses, i.e., the probability of a head is $\frac{1}{2}$, or 0.50. The probability of a tail is $P =$ _____. If the first production run of 10,000 parts resulted in 100 defective parts, the quality control engineer would no doubt estimate the probability of a defective to be _____.

$\frac{1}{2}$, or 0.50

100/10,000 or $P = 0.01$

3

In the past two decades, a new interpretation of probability called *subjective* or *personal* probability has been growing rapidly in the area of business decision making. Subjective probability measures the *strength of personal belief*. For example, a weather forecaster might state that (in his opinion) the chance of rain tomorrow is 10 percent, or $P = 0.10$. Another forecaster using the same set of weather data and maps might put the probability at 0.20. An economist after reviewing inventory level, unemployment, and so on might indicate that there is a 40 percent chance of a recession during the forthcoming summer. Another economist using the same data might believe the probability of a recession is 0.20. These degrees of belief are called _____ probabilities. The use of the subjective approach to probability will be examined in more detail in the chapter on decision making under uncertainty (Chapter 11), and in Chapter 12.

subjective or personal

4

It will become apparent in the following discussion that there is no necessary conflict between the two interpretations. In fact, in many problems, both the objective and subjective notions will be of value. Many of the rules for manipulating and combining probabilities apply both to objective and subjective probabilities.

The science of probability has been of concern to mathematicians since the early 1600's. Much of the early study was devoted to mathematical problems involving games of cards, dice, roulette, and other games of chance. Many mathematicians earned their livelihood working out and instructing wealthy patrons in "knowing the odds." Marquis de Laplace (1749–1827) interpreted probability "simply as a fraction whose numerator is the number of favorable cases and whose denominator is the number of all the cases possible." To illustrate, suppose there are four cards lying face down on a table. There is a spade, a diamond, a heart, and a club. What is the probability of selecting one of the cards at random and finding it to be a diamond? _____

$\frac{1}{4}$, or 0.25

5

These probabilities are designated as *a priori*. A priori probabilities then can be determined *before* an experiment, trial, or any sampling is done. For example, it is common knowledge that a coin has a head on one side and a tail on the other side. It can be reasoned beforehand, therefore, that should a large number of coins be tossed in the air about half of them will have a head showing face up. That is, $P(\text{head}) = \frac{1}{2}$. It should be noted that *a priori probabilities are confined to events that can be repeated and have equally likely outcomes.*

A single die has six sides numbered 1, 2, 3, 4, 5, or 6. How many *equally likely* outcomes are there? _____. What is the probability that a 4 will appear on a throw of the die? _____. Can this probability be considered a priori? (yes/no) _____. Explain _____
_____

6
6
⅙ yes
Probability can be determined before an experiment is conducted.

6 _____

However, in many business problems, it is inconceivable that the probability of an event can be determined beforehand. And furthermore, the equally likely assumption may not be realistic. For example, it is not realistic to assume that before a new model color television set is introduced on the market, an equal number of persons will buy one, two, and three sets for their homes next year. Thus, two characteristics of this early approach to probability which may not be applicable to many real business problems are _____
_____ and _____.

(in any order) probability of an outcome cannot be determined beforehand and probability of various outcomes are not equally likely

7 _____

A Russian mathematician, A. N. Kolmogorov, suggested a *relative frequency* interpretation of probability in the 1930's which has since become synonymous with the objective interpretation. A probability is interpreted as the *relative frequency resulting from a long series of trials or observations*. This interpretation of probability differs in one important respect from the earlier classical approach. The classical notion is that the probability of an outcome happening can be determined (before/after) _____
_____ an experiment. The relative frequency approach is that the probability is computed (before/after) _____ a series of trials or observations. Probabilities computed after a sample (trials) (experiment) (observations) are called *posteriori*, or *empirical* probabilities. Thus, the relative frequency interpretation of probabilities relies on past experience.

before
after

A probability computed prior to throwing a die can be considered an exact probability. A probability computed from sampling data cannot be exact, but rather it is only an estimate. If, out of a sample of 2,000 employees, 1,600 were in favor of a guaranteed annual wage, the probability of 0.80 is only an estimate because a larger sample would give a more precise (and, no doubt, different) probability, such as 0.79 or 0.82. Thus, empirical probabilities can be considered as being (exact/estimates) _____
_____ and a priori probabilities as being (exact/estimates) _____

estimates
exact

8 _____

A canning company keeps a constant check on the weight of the content of the cans. Although the machine is set to give the weight specified on the label, the content of some cans is under what is specified and others are overweight. The results of frequent checks at the beginning of the

0.05
.85
.10
1.00

Content	Number of Cans	Probability of Occurrence
Underweight	100	0.
Correct weight	1,700	.
Overweight	200	.
Total		.

new canning season were organized into the previous table. Compute the probabilities and record the answers in the spaces provided. What is the probability that a can picked at random will be overweight? _____. Is it an a priori or empirical probability? _____. Are the outcomes equally likely? (yes/no) _____.

200/2,000 or 1/10 or 0.10
empirical
no

9 ───

As noted in the previous example, the sum of the probabilities for all possible outcomes cannot exceed _____. One six-sided die is tossed. The probability of an 8 appearing is _____. Thus, the lowest value a probability assumes is _____ and the highest _____. Is the probability of −1.0 possible? (yes/no) _____.

1.0
0.0   0
1
no

10 ───

In the problem cited previously, a can was either underweight, overweight, or had the correct weight. Thus, the outcomes of an event are considered to be *mutually exclusive*, meaning that a can selected at random cannot *at the same time* be underweight, overweight, and have the correct weight. To put it another way, *mutually exclusive outcomes means that simultaneous occurrence is not possible*. Referring to the random selection of one of the four cards lying face down on the table (a diamond, a spade, a club, and a heart), are the outcomes mutually exclusive? (yes/no) _____.
Explain _____
_____

yes
A card chosen at random can only be one suit.

11 ───

English logician, J. Venn, (1834–88) developed a diagram to portray graphically the mutually exclusive concept and various other rules for combining probabilities. To construct a Venn diagram, a space is first enclosed which represents the total of all possible outcomes. This space may be any shape and is called the *sample space*. Some outcome (such as a tail appearing on the toss of a coin) is called a *sample point*. Thus, the total of all sample points equals the _____.

sample space

The following Venn diagram represents the mutually exclusive concept. If a head (event A) occurs, a tail (event B) does not. There is no overlapping of events, i.e., the events are _____

mutually exclusive

12 ───

The next Venn diagram shows the possible outcomes on the roll of a die. Does the diagram, called a _____ _____ diagram, account for all possible outcomes? (yes/no) _____. The total area encompassed by the heavy black line is called the _____.

Venn

yes

sample space

The individual areas marked A, B, C, D, E, and F are called _____
_____.

The probability that event A would occur is _____. The probability that event A would not occur (written ~A) is _____.

13 ——————————————————————————

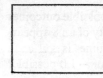

Referring again to the previous problem of four cards (a diamond, a club, a spade, and a heart) lying face down on a table, draw a Venn diagram in the space provided to show the mutually exclusive nature of the outcomes.

14 ——————————————————————————

Rules for manipulating and combining probabilities

Several computations involving probabilities have already been examined. In frame #8 the probability of a can selected at random being underweight (event A) was computed to be 0.05. Other probabilities were: correct weight (event B) 0.85, and overweight (event C) 0.10. It was noted that:

$$P(A) + P(B) + P(C) = 1$$

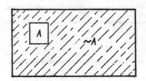

Also, the probability that a can selected at random was underweight $P(A)$, plus the probability it was not underweight, written $P(\sim A)$, must equal 1. Shown symbolically:

$$P(A) + P(\sim A) = 1$$

The Venn diagram might appear as shown.

$P(A) + P(\sim A) = 1$ can be revised to read:

$$P(A) = 1 - P(\sim A)$$

The rule is often referred to as the *complement rule*. The probability that an ace will be chosen at random from a standard deck of 52 cards is 4/52. What is the probability that it will not be chosen? _____, found by _____. This is called the _____ rule.

15 ——————————————————————————

In the foregoing discussion, another rule in dealing with probabilities was used but it was not identified as the *addition* rule. Returning to a simple example to illustrate it, a head (event A) or a tail (event B) may occur on the toss of a coin. The outcomes are mutually exclusive. Then:

$$P(A \text{ or } B) = P(A) + P(B)$$

So, the probability of a head (A) or a tail (B) (written $P(A \text{ or } B)$, occurring is 1, found by ½ + ½.

Recall that the probability a can would be underweight is 0.05, the correct weight

0.85, and overweight 0.10. What is the probability that a can selected at random will contain the correct weight or be overweight? _____. (Note the addition rule applies even though the letters are different and there are more than two possible outcomes.)

Ages of the respondents to a questionnaire were grouped as follows:

Number of Respondents	Ages
40	Under 18 years
100	18 up to 30 years
30	30 up to 50 years
20	50 up to 70 years
10	70 years and over

What is the probability that if a questionnaire were chosen at random the respondent would be either under 18 years, or 30 up to 50 years, or 70 years and over? _____ _____. This is an application of the _____ rule. What is the probability that the respondent is not in one of these three age groups? _____. This is an illustration of the _____ rule. The outcomes are _____ exclusive.

16 ─────────────────────────────

The adjacent _____ diagram illustrates two outcomes which are not mutually exclusive, i.e., there is an overlapping of outcomes. This means that there is some chance that both A and B can occur at the same time. It is usually written $P(A,B)$ or $P(A \text{ and } B)$, and is called the *compound* event, or the *joint* probability of A and B. It seems logical that to compute the probability of A or B that the joint probability of A and B should be subtracted or it will be added twice. Thus, to compute the probability of A or B:

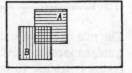

$$P(A \text{ or } B) = P(A) + P(B) - P(A,B)$$

Venn

17 ─────────────────────────────

Again, a simple illustration involving a standard deck of cards containing 52 cards. The probability that a card chosen at random from the deck is either a king or a diamond is 16/52 or 0.3077, found by: (event A is a king, event B is a diamond).

$$P(A \text{ or } B) = P(A) + P(B) - P(A,B)$$
$$= 4/52 + 13/52 - 1/52$$

Are the possible outcomes mutually exclusive or nonmutually exclusive? _____ _____ exclusive. Explain _____

What is the probability that a card selected at random is either a jack or a diamond or a club? _____.

nonmutually
The king of diamonds is both a king and a diamond. Because of this overlapping, the joint probability of A and B is subtracted to prevent it from being added twice. 28/52, found by $4/52 + 13/52 + 13/52 - 1/52 - 1/52$.

18 ─────────────────────────────

Two coins are to be tossed in the air—either simultaneously or one and then the other. The action, or outcome, of one coin will in no way affect the other. This concept is known as *statistical independence*. If the two outcomes are independent, then the probability of a head occurring on one coin, written $P(A)$, and the probability of a head occurring on the other coin, written $P(B)$, is:

$$P(A \text{ and } B) = P(A) \cdot P(B)$$
$$= 1/2 \times 1/2$$
$$= 1/4$$

This can be shown by listing all of the possible outcomes. Two heads is only one of the four possible outcomes.

	H	H
or	H	T
or	T	H
or	T	T

The foregoing illustrates the *multiplication rule* when the outcomes are independent. Using the multiplication rule, design an equation and then solve for the probability that three heads will appear on the toss of three coins.

The equation is _____

The probabilities are: _____

The answer is _____

$P(A \text{ and } B \text{ and } C)$
$= P(A) \cdot P(B) \cdot P(C)$
$\frac{1}{2} \times \frac{1}{2} \times \frac{1}{2}$
$\frac{1}{8}$ or 0.125

19

The rule of multiplication is also used when the probabilities are *conditional*. To illustrate, suppose a scheme has been devised to raise money for charity. A total of 100 sealed boxes are to be placed on a table, and the donors may buy one or more of them. There are prizes in 10 of the boxes and the remaining 90 are empty. A prominent donor has the privilege of selecting the first two boxes. One might wonder what his chance is of winning two prizes. The probability that he will win a prize on the first draw, designated as $P(A)$ is 10/100. Then the probability that he will win two prizes depends on whether he won a prize on the first draw. Thus, the probability of a prize on the second draw is conditional on the results of the first draw. This conditional probability is designated as $P(B|A)$ and is interpreted as the probability of B happening given that A has happened. The probability of winning two prizes on the first two draws is found by:

$$P(A \text{ and } B) = P(A) \cdot P(B|A)$$
$$= \frac{10}{100} \times \frac{9}{99}$$
$$= \frac{1}{110}, \text{ or slightly less than 1 percent}$$

Note that the probability $P(B|A)$ of 9/99 assumes that a prize was chosen the first draw and only 9 prizes were left in the remaining 99 boxes. The concept of conditional probability is, therefore, based on the assumption that the two (or more) events are (dependent/independent) _____.

dependent

A survey is to be conducted by interviewing 10 executives. One executive is in the mining industry, three in the service industry, and the remaining in manufacturing. The names of the executives to be interviewed will be picked at random. What is the probability that the first two executives chosen will be in the manufacturing industry?

The equation is _____.
The probabilities (fractions) are _____.
The answer is _____.
What is the probability that three executives in the manufacturing industry will be chosen on the first three selections? _____.

$P(A \text{ and } B) = P(A) \cdot P(B|A)$

$\dfrac{6}{10} \times \dfrac{5}{9}$

⅓ or 0.33

⅙ or 0.17, found by
$\dfrac{6}{10} \times \dfrac{5}{9} \times \dfrac{4}{8}$

20

Permutations and combinations

Determining the total number of possible outcomes in a problem involving probabilities may be difficult. Rules of *permutations* and *combinations* merely facilitate counting. Both permutations and combinations use a notation called "*n* factorial." This is written *n*! It means the product of $n(n-1)(n-2)(n-3) \ldots [n-(n-1)]$. For example, 6! would be computed by $6(6-1)(6-2)(6-3)(6-4)[6-(6-1)]$. That is, $6 \cdot 5 \cdot 4 \cdot 3 \cdot 2 \cdot 1 = 720$. What does 4! equal? _____.

24

The numbers $4 \cdot 3 \cdot 2 \cdot 1$ are products. Therefore, they can be canceled when in the numerator and denominator. To illustrate:

$$\frac{5!3!}{4!} = \frac{5 \cdot \cancel{4} \cdot 3 \cdot 2 \cdot 1(\cancel{3} \cdot \cancel{2} \cdot \cancel{1})}{\cancel{4} \cdot \cancel{3} \cdot \cancel{2} \cdot \cancel{1}} = 30$$

$$\frac{6!2}{3!} = \text{_____}$$

240

21

Permutations.   Three machines (a grinder, a drill press, and a shaper), are to be placed on the floor of the plant. The problem is to determine how many different ways the three machines can be placed on the floor. The number of permutations is determined by:

$$P = \frac{n!}{(n-r)!}$$

In this equation, P is the number of permutations or ways the machines can be placed; n is the number of machines; and r represents the number of machines to be placed on the floor at a time. There are three machines ($n = 3$), and all three are going to be placed on the floor ($r = 3$). Note that there are three different machines making repetition impossible. For example, it is not possible to place three grinders on the floor. It should be noted before solving the problem that, by definition, $0! = 1! = 1$. Then:

$$P = \frac{n!}{(n-r)!} = \frac{3!}{(3-3)!} = \frac{3!}{0!} = \frac{3!}{1!} = 6$$

The six ways are ABC, ACB, BCA, BAC, CBA, and CAB.

The formula for permutations is applicable when it is desired to count the number of ways (permutations) of *n* things taken *r* at a time. The ordering of the different items is important, i.e., ABC is one order of the items, BCA is another order, and so on.

It has been decided that only five colors are to be used in decorating an office building. The colors are always to be used in groups of three, such as red, yellow, and blue.

60, found by $\dfrac{5!}{(5-3)!}$

How many ways can the five colors be arranged in groups of three? _____
_____.

22 _____

If repetitions are permitted, then $P = n^r$. To illustrate, two letters, A and B, are to be taken two at a time. With repetitions, such as AA, there are four ways (permutations) possible, found by 2^2. The four ways would be AB, BA, AA, and BB. If repetitions were not allowed, how many ways can the two letters be arranged? _____

2

_____.

In the previous frame, it was found that there were 60 different ways five colors could be used three colors at a time. If repetitions were allowed (such as red, yellow, yellow), how many permutations could there be? _____.

125, found by 5^3

23 _____

Combinations. In computing the number of permutations of n things taken r at a time, the order of things was important. In the office decoration problem, the decorator could use red on the floor, yellow on the walls, and blue on the ceiling in one room, and in another room the order could be changed to yellow on the floor, blue on the walls, and red on the ceiling, and so on. It was calculated that there were 60 such permutations of five colors taken three at a time.

Suppose the decorator has just decided that a combination of any three colors will be used only once in the building. This means that if red, blue, and yellow are used in Room No. 6, no other room can be decorated with these three colors. In effect, the many different ways of ordering the three colors is being disregarded. That is, the combination of red, blue, and yellow is considered the same as blue, yellow, and red. One might now ask, how many different *combinations* of the five colors taken three at a time are possible. The answer is 10, found by:

$$C = \frac{n!}{r!(n-r)!} = \frac{5!}{3!(5-3)!}$$

210, found by $\dfrac{10!}{4!\,(10-4)!}$

There are 10 union stewards in the plant and 4 are to be picked at random to attend a convention. How many different combinations of stewards are possible? _____.
(Note that a combination recognizes a group of four stewards comprised of Smith, Jones, Miller, and Stevens is the same as Jones, Stevens, Miller, and Smith.)

Final Self-Review Examination

First, answer all of the questions. Then check your answers against those given at the end of this chapter. Scoring: 10 problems × 10 points each = 100 possible points.

24. Discuss the difference between the objective and subjective interpretation of probability.

_____
_____
_____
_____
_____

25. The following is called a (a)_____
_____.

    The probabilities are (mutually exclusive/non-mutually exclusive. (b)_____
    _____. The block A is called a (sample space/ sample point) (c)_____
    _____ _____
    _____.

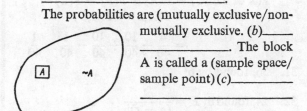

26. A random sample revealed that 100 parts were poorly machined, 700 parts were satisfactorily machined, and 200 parts were exceptionally well machined. It would, no doubt, be estimated that the probability of an exceptionally well machined part is (a)_____.
    The probabilities are considered as being (a priori/empirical) (b)_____.

27. Four disks were polished on one side but left dull on the other side. If the disks were tossed in the air, what is the probability that all four would land with polished sides facing up? (a)_____. Are the outcomes dependent or independent? (b)_____
    _____.

28. It is known that 3 parts in a batch of 10 parts are defective. What is the probability that the first three parts selected at random will be defective? (a)_____. Are the outcomes conditional or nonconditional? (b)_____
    _____.

29. A round-robin tennis match involving 10 people must be scheduled. (A round robin means that each person plays every other person. Usually, the person winning the most number of matches wins the grand prize.) How many matches must be scheduled? (Hint: If Sam plays Joe, it is the same as Joe playing Sam.)
    _____.

30. Four firms are considering merging to form one company. A ten-man delegation, including the president and nine other men, from each of the four firms met to discuss the proposed merger. The four firms are Armcoe Ltd., Smith Steel, NoFarm Products, and Casper Aluminum. It was decided to divide into small committees of three members each to study various aspects of the merger. Each committee is to be picked at random. The rules committee is to be chosen first. What is the probability that the first member of the rules committee chosen will be either a president, or a man from Smith Steel, or a man from Casper Aluminum? (a)_____.

31. The Intelligence Bureau is designing a secret code based on six letters—A, B, C, D, E, and F. Only two letters are to be transmitted, such as AA, or AB, or BA. Note that repetitions are permitted. How many code signals are possible? _____.

32. The production planning department has the problem of determining the most efficient way of assembling four pieces into a sub-assembly. The four pieces can be assembled in any order, such as 1, 2, 3, 4, or 2, 1, 4, 3, and so on. How many different ways can the four pieces be assembled? _____.

33. The same production planning department has another problem concerning soldering. There are six parts. The first operation will involve connecting two parts with a wire, such as (A)(B). In this operation, it does not matter which two are connected (AB or AC or CD or DF, etc.). Note, however, that connecting AB is the same as connecting BA. How many ways can the six parts be connected, taking them two at a time?
    _____.

Answers to Final Self-Review Examination

24. The objective interpretation of probability is that a probability can be determined beforehand (a priori), such as the probability of a four spot appearing on the toss of a die. A probability can also be determined on the basis of experience. An illustration of this is the probability of a defective after observing that 100 out of a sample of 1,000 parts selected at random were defective.

    The subjective interpretation of probability is one of personal belief. For example, if an executive strongly believes that the level of demand for a multicolored automobile tire will be high, he might assign a probability of 0.90 to this high level, 0.07 to an average level of demand, and 0.03 to a low level of demand.

25. (a) Venn diagram
    (b) mutually exclusive
    (c) sample point

26. (a) 0.20
    (b) empirical

27. (a) 1/16, found by $1/2 \times 1/2 \times 1/2 \times 1/2$
    (b) independent

28. (a) $6/720 = 1/120 \ (\cong 0.008)$ found by

$$P(A \text{ and } B \text{ and } C) = P(A) \times P(B \mid A) \times P(C \mid B)$$
$$= \frac{3}{10} \times \frac{2}{9} \times \frac{1}{8}$$

(b) conditional

29. 45, found by $C = \dfrac{n!}{r!(n-r)!}$
    $$= \frac{10!}{2!8!}$$

30. 22/40, found by
    $$P(A \text{ or } B \text{ or } C) = P(A) + P(B) + P(C) - P(A,B) - P(A,C)$$
    $$= \frac{4}{40} + \frac{10}{40} + \frac{10}{40} - \frac{1}{40} - \frac{1}{40}$$

31. 36, found by 6^2

32. 24, found by $P = \dfrac{n!}{(n-r)!}$
    $$= \frac{4!}{(4-4)!}$$
    $$= \frac{4!}{1} \text{ (by definition)}$$

33. 15, found by $C = \dfrac{n!}{r!(n-r)!}$
    $$= \frac{6!}{2!(6-2)!}$$

Probability distributions

1

The *Bernoulli, or binomial probability distribution*, the *Poisson probability distribution*, and the *normal probability distribution* are but three probability distributions. The application of these theoretical distributions to probability-type problems can assist the quality control engineer in making a decision to accept or reject an incoming lot of transistors based on the discovery of, say, two defective transistors in a sample of 100 selected at random from the lot. The public opinion pollsters and the marketing research analysts use various theoretical probability distributions (as will be shown in the following chapters) in preelection polling and in analyzing consumer surveys and test market data.

THE BERNOULLI OR BINOMIAL PROBABILITY DISTRIBUTION

The Bernoulli probability distribution (named after Jacques Bernoulli, who in the 1600's also developed the concept of permutations) is applicable when only two outcomes are possible. For example, in a true-false test, an answer to a question is either right or wrong. Other illustrations:

Valve stem is defective	Will not vote for the incumbent
Valve stem is not defective	Will vote for the incumbent
Does not like the toothpaste	Cannot identify the brand name
Does like the toothpaste	Can identify the brand name

Since there is no measurement involved, the Bernoulli probability distribution, also called the _____ probability distribution is a discrete distribution. Could a distribution of the tensile strengths of wires be described by a binomial distribution? (yes/no) _____. Explain _____
_____

binomial

no Tensile strengths are measurable; thus, the data are continuous.

2

The binomial probability distribution can be expressed several different ways.

$$(q + p)^n \quad \text{or}$$

$$\Sigma_n C_r(p)^r(q)^{n-r} \quad \text{or} \quad \sum \frac{n!}{r!(n-r)!} (p)^r(q)^{n-r}$$

To illustrate, suppose that it is desired to compute the probability of guessing 0, 1, 2, 3, and 4 questions correct out of four questions on a true-false test and to construct a binomial probability distribution. First, to compute the probability of guessing four out of four correctly using the formula:

$$P(r) = \frac{n!}{r!(n-r)!} (p)^r(q)^{n-r}$$

where n is the total number of items, or 4 questions in this problem.

51

r is the number of correct answers (4) out of the total.
n − r is the number of incorrect answers (0) out of the total, found by 4–4.
p is the probability of guessing an answer correctly (0.50).
q is the probability of not guessing an answer correctly (0.50).

Thus, to compute the probability of guessing 4 out of 4 correctly:

$$P(r) = \frac{n!}{r!(n-r)!}(p)^r(q)^{n-r}$$

$$P(r) = \frac{4!}{4!(4-4)!}(0.50)^4(0.50)^{4-4}$$

$$= \frac{4!}{4!0!}\qquad(0.50)^4(0.50)^0$$

recall from the previous chapter that 0! = 1. Also, $(p)^0$ or $(q)^0$ = 1. Thus, $(0.50)^0$ = 1.
Then:

$$= (1)(0.50)^4(1)$$
$$= 0.0625$$

Compute the probability of guessing three out of four correctly 0. _____
___, and the probability of guessing 0 out of four correctly. 0. _____
___.

.2500, found by (4)
(0.50)³(0.50)¹
.0625, found by (1)
(0.50)⁰(0.50)⁴

The left margin answers:
.2500, found by (4) $(0.50)^3(0.50)^1$
.0625, found by (1) $(0.50)^0(0.50)^4$

3

The complete distribution of probabilities for guessing 0, 1, 2, 3, and 4 correct out of
four follows. A histogram has been constructed to show the symmetrical nature of the
distribution.

HISTOGRAM REPRESENTING THE
BINOMIAL PROBABILITY DISTRIBUTION,
$n = 4$, $p = 0.50$.

BINOMIAL PROBABILITY DISTRIBUTION
FOR $n = 4$, $p = 0.50$

Number of Correct Guesses	Probability
0	0.0625
1	.2500
2	.3750
3	.2500
4	.0625
	1.0000

The binomial expansion $(q + p)^n$ could have been used to find the probabilities. [The
expansion is also written $(p + q)^n$.] Recall from algebra:

$$(q + p)^1 = q + p$$
$$(q + p)^2 = q^2 + 2qp + p^2$$
$$(q + p)^3 = q^3 + 3q^2p + 3qp^2 + p^3$$
$$(q + p)^4 = q^4 + 4q^3p + 6q^2p^2 + 4qp^3 + p^4$$

and so on.
In this problem, q is the probability of guessing the answer correctly and p is the

probability of guessing it incorrectly. The probabilities shown in the previous table for $n = 4$ could have been computed using the binomial expansion $(q + p)^4$. The first term q^4 is $(0.50)^4$, or 0.0625, and is the probability of guessing none correct out of four. The second term of $4q^3p$ represents the probability of guessing one correct out of four, and so on. Without referring to the answer given in the previous table, compute the probability of guessing three correct out of four using the binomial expansion. 0. _____
_____, found by _____.

.2500
$4qp^3$ or $4(0.5)(0.5)^3$

---

4 _____

The numbers in front of each of the terms are called *binomial coefficients*. The binomial coefficients in the previous problem where $n = 4$, are 1, 4, 6, 4, and 1. When q and p are 0.50, the terms yield a symmetrical binomial probability distribution. These binomial coefficients can be obtained from *Pascal's triangle* (developed by Blaise Pascal in the 17th century).

Number in Sample n	Binomial Coefficients											Sum
1						1	1					2
2					1	2	1					4
3				1	3	3	1					8
4			1	4	6	4	1					16
5		1	5	10	10	5	1					32
6	1	6	15	20	15	6	1					64
7	1	7	21	35	35	21	7	1				128
8	1	8	28	56	70	56	28	8	1			256
9	1	9	36	84	126	126	84	36	9	1		512
10	1	10	45	120	210	252	210	120	45	10	1	1,024

The terms for the binomial expansion for 10 true-false questions would be $(q + p)^{10}$. To find the probability of getting 0 correct out of 10, using Pascal's triangle, the first term would be $1q^{10}$. And, $q^{10} = (0.5)^{10} = 0.0009766$. The second term would be $10q^9p^1$ and represents the probability of guessing 1 out of 10 correct. Thus, $10(0.0009766) = 0.0098$. Note that the sum of the powers applied to q and $p = n$. That is, $9 + 1 = 10$.

Using the binomial expansion (and Pascal's triangle), the next number (45) would be the binomial coefficient for _____ correct out of 10. The term would be _____. The probability of guessing two out of ten correct is 0. _____.

2
$45q^8p^2$
.0439, found by
45(0.0009766)

---

5 _____

The main purpose of the foregoing discussion was to show that a binomial probability distribution is a theoretical distribution which can be generated mathematically using the binomial expansion method. In practice, however, these calculations need not be done, as a table for the binomial distribution is available (Appendix Table VII). To find the probability of guessing 2 out of 10 in a true-false test ($n = 10$, $r = 2$), it is first necessary to locate the n of 10. Then move down to the r of 2. Finally, move horizontally in that row until the number under the p of 0.50 is located. It is 0.0439, the same as calculated in frame #4. What is the probability of guessing 6 out of 10 correctly in a true-false test? 0. _____. This means if there were 10,000 students

.2051

2,051

in a class, and a 10-question true-false test were given, approximately _____ _____ students would guess 6 out of 10 correctly. (This assumes that the students had no knowledge of the subject and were just guessing.)

6

The probabilities for the 10-question true-false test are presented in the following table. Complete the table. Then draw a histogram representing the binomial distribution.

.1172
.0439
.0098
.0010
1.0000

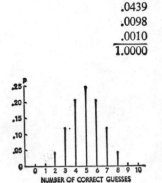

NUMBER OF CORRECT GUESSES

HISTOGRAM REPRESENTING THE BINOMIAL PROBABILITY DISTRIBUTION FOR $n = 10$, $p = 0.50$

BINOMIAL PROBABILITY DISTRIBUTION FOR, $n = 10$, $p = 0.50$

Number of Correct Guesses	Probability
0	0.0010
1	.0098
2	.0439
3	.1172
4	.2051
5	.2461
6	.2051
7	——
8	——
9	——
10	——
Approximate Total	——

7

38 percent

The instructor indicated that 60 percent or more (6 or more out of 10) will be a passing grade in the test. Approximately what percent of the students will pass? _____

8

The probability of an event occurring (p) and the probability of an event not occurring (q) may not be equal (0.50). If the probabilities are not equal, the binomial distribution is not symmetrical but instead is skewed. If the probability of a defective part (p) is 0.05, q (the probability of a nondefective part) is 0.95. The binomial expansion method may be used to determine the probability of 0, 1, and 2 defectives chosen at random out of two ($n = 2$). (Refer to frame #3 for the binomial expansion.)

The probabilities of:	0	1	2 defectives
are computed by:	q^2	$+ 2qp$	$+ p^2$
inserting q and p:	$(0.95)^2$	$+ 2(0.95 \times 0.05)$	$+ (0.05)^2$
the probabilities are:	0.9025	$+ 0.0950$	$+ 0.0025 = 1.0$

Of course, the total of all possible outcomes must equal 1.0. As noted previously, it is not necessary to calculate the probabilities. They have already been determined and are in Appendix Table VII for $n = 2$, $p = 0.05$. Again, note that the distribution of probabilities is skewed.

BINOMIAL PROBABILITY DISTRIBUTION
FOR $n = 2$, $p = 0.05$

Number of Defective Parts	Probability
0	0.9025
1	.0950
2	.0025
Total	1.0000

HISTOGRAM REPRESENTING THE
BINOMIAL PROBABILITY
DISTRIBUTION FOR
$n = 2$, $p = 0.05$

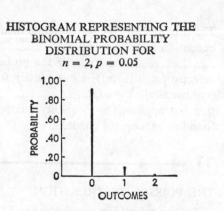

A multiple-choice examination consisting of 10 questions has been designed. There are four possible answers to each question. Thus, $p = 0$. _____. Assume that none of the students taking the multiple-choice test attended class or studied for the examination (a common occurrence). Design a binomial probability distribution for guessing 0, 1, 2, ... 10 correct out of 10 on the examination. Then draw a histogram representing the distribution.

.25, found by ¼

.0563
.1877
.2816
.2503
.1460
.0584
.0162
.0031
.0004
.0000
.0000
1.0000

BINOMIAL PROBABILITY DISTRIBUTION
FOR $n = 10$, $p = 0.25$

0	0. _____
1	_____
2	_____
3	_____
4	_____
5	_____
6	_____
7	_____
8	_____
9	_____
10	_____
Approximate Total	_____

HISTOGRAM REPRESENTING THE
BINOMIAL PROBABILITY
DISTRIBUTION FOR
$n = 10$, $p = 0.25$

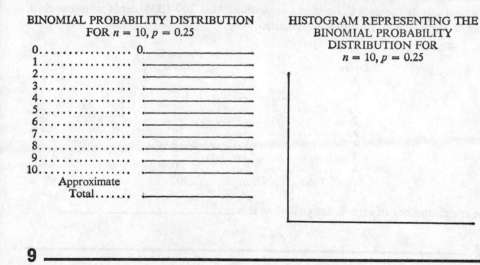

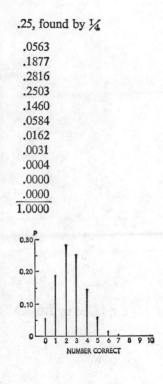

9 _____

The instructor giving the multiple choice test has set 60 percent and above as the passing grades, i.e., 6, 7, 8, 9, or 10 out of ten correct. If there were 100 students in the class, theoretically about how many students would pass the examination? Approximately _____. (This compares with about 38 out of 100 (from Frame #7) who would pass a true-false test with 60 percent or above.)

2 students, found by adding 0.0162, 0.0031, 0.0004, 0.0000, and 0.0000.

10 _____

In summary, a binomial probability distribution is also called a _____ __ probability distribution. It is applicable when (one/two/three or more) _____ _____ outcomes are possible. The Bernoulli (binomial) probability distribution is a (discrete/continuous) _____ distribution. When $p = 0.50$, the binomial distribution is (symmetrical/skewed) _____.

Bernoulli
two

discrete
symmetrical

The probabilities for the binomial distribution can be determined using the binomial expansion method, or by _____

reading the probabilities
from a table

_____. If the probability of a "success" (guessing correctly, not defective, and so on) is not exactly 0.50, the Bernoulli probability distribution is

skewed

(symmetrical/skewed) _____. This theoretical probability distribution has applications in quality control statistics sampling, and tests of hypotheses found in subsequent chapters.

11

THE POISSON DISTRIBUTION

Originated by Simeon Poisson in 1837, the Poisson probability distribution is another discrete distribution. It is used to describe such phenomena as the distribution of the number of errors in IBM punched cards or the number of scratches and other imperfections in newly painted panels. To apply the Poisson distribution, n must be large, i.e., a large number of IBM punched cards or a large number of painted panels. And, p (the probability of a defect, error, etc.) must be small.

Another characteristic is that there can be 0, 1, 2, 3, 4, ... errors on the card or imperfections in the panel. To illustrate, assume that 300 IBM cards were checked, using a verifier, with the following results:

Errors X	Number of Cards f
0	162
1	88
2	35
3	10
4	3
5	2
6	0
Total	300

0.7, found by 210/300

The mean number of errors, designated as μ is _____.

12

The mean (μ) is needed to construct a theoretical Poisson probability distribution. The probability of say two errors can be computed by:

$$P(X) = \frac{\mu^X e^{-\mu}}{X!}$$

where

μ is the mean number of occurrences.

X is the number of occurrences being considered (2 in this case).

e is the base of the natural (Naperian) logarithms (2.71828).

$X!$ is X factorial (and in this case is 2 factorial).

$$P(2) = \frac{(0.7)^2 (2.71828)^{-0.7}}{2 \cdot 1}$$

The calculations for the probability of two errors and the probabilities of 0, 1, . . . errors have been made and placed in a table. Refer to Appendix Table VI. Reading horizontally, locate $\mu = 0.7$. The probability of no errors is 0.496585. The probability of one error is 0. _____. Instead of determining the probability of two errors using the previous equation, the value read from the table is 0. _____.

.347610

.121663

13 ——————————————————————————————————————

Suppose that records were kept on the number of imperfections per panel which had to be repaired before the panel was shipped to the buyer. The distribution of the number of imperfections (such as burrs, paint globs, and unpainted surfaces) approximated a Poisson distribution. That is, a large number of the panels had no imperfections, some had one imperfection, very few panels had two imperfections, and so on.

The mean number of imperfections per panel was computed to be 0.5. The Poisson probability distribution is (to simplify calculations, copy probabilities to the first *three* figures only):

Number of Imperfections X	Probability of X
0	0. _____
1	_____
2	_____
3	_____
4	_____
5	_____

.606
.303
.075
.012
.001
.000

14 ——————————————————————————————————————

An order for 1,000 panels has been received. The cost department must estimate the total cost of repairing the panels *before* the work begins. Past experience revealed that each imperfection costs 10¢ to repair. What is the estimated total cost? (Hint: One imperfection costs 10¢, three imperfections 30¢ to repair, and so on.) _____.

$49.30, found by:

X		
0	606 × 0 =	$0
1	303 × 10¢ =	30.30
2	75 × 20¢ =	15.00
3	12 × 30¢ =	3.60
4	1 × 40¢ =	0.40

15 ——————————————————————————————————————

The Poisson probability distribution for a μ of 5.0 follows. Plot the probability distributions for a μ of 0.5 and a μ of 2.0 on the same graph.

It should be stressed again that the Poisson probability distribution involves counts (discrete data). *Thus, only the points on the graph are important. The fact that lines connect the points does not indicate that there are probabilities between the points.*

An analysis of the adjacent graph containing probability distributions, called _____

_____ probability distributions, reveals that all three are (symmetrical/skewed) _____.

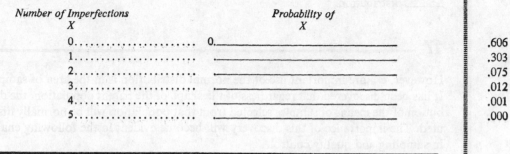

However, note as the mean (μ) becomes larger, the Poisson distribution tends to

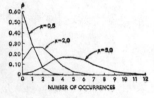

Poisson

skewed

approach a symmetrical distribution. Reference to the various Poisson distributions in Appendix Table VI reemphasizes this.

Before any Poisson probability distribution is constructed, it is necessary to know one value—namely, the _____.

mean, denoted as μ

16

THE NORMAL PROBABILITY DISTRIBUTION

The preceding discussion dealt with two discrete probability distributions namely, the _____ and the _____ distributions. Conversely, *the normal probability distribution is applicable to measurable data.* Examples of data which tend to follow a normal pattern are the tensile strengths of wire, weight of male children 10 years old, and the length of fingerling trout. Thus, since this type of data can assume fractional values, such as 1,003.583 pounds tensile strength, the normal distribution is a (discrete/continuous) _____ _____ distribution.

binonomial and Poisson

continuous

17

However, a more important use of the normal distribution is in the area of sampling. It has been discovered that regardless of the shape of the parent population, the distribution of the means of samples selected from that population will be normally distributed. The importance of this discovery will become evident in the following chapters in sampling and quality control.

The equation for the normal probability distribution is:

$$Y = \frac{1}{\sigma\sqrt{2\pi}} e^{-\frac{1}{2}(X-\mu)^2/\sigma^2}$$

where μ = mean, σ = standard deviation, π = 3.14159 $\cdots$, e = 2.71828 $\cdots$

Note that the μ and the standard deviation σ are needed to construct a normal distribution. In contrast, what was needed to develop a Poisson distribution? _____ _____. A binomial distribution? _____ _____ and _____.

The mean number of errors (imperfections) designated as μ.
The probability of success, designated as p and the number of frequencies (n).

18

To construct a normal distribution using the formula would be a formidable task because of the large number of calculations necessary. (The distribution is continuous, meaning that there is an infinite number of possible values X could assume.) A table of the areas under the normal curve has been developed to facilitate the construction and use of the normal distribution (Appendix Table IV).

The table has been standardized to make it applicable to any problem involving a normal distribution. To use the table, various values must be transformed into a standard measure called z. This standard measure, often called the *z value*, the *standard normal deviate*, the *standard deviate* or the *z transformation*, is found by:

$$z = \frac{X - \mu}{\sigma}$$

To illustrate, suppose a distribution of the weights of ball bearings follows a normal pattern with a mean of 100 ounces and a standard deviation of 10 ounces. One might ask, what proportion of the weights were between 100 ounces and, say, 110 ounces. ($\mu = 100$, $\sigma = 10$, and $X = 110$)

Show the formula, insert the values, and find the z value.

$z = $ _____ $=$ _____ $=$ _____

$$\frac{X - \mu}{\sigma} = \frac{110 - 100}{10} = 1.00$$

19 _____

Now, referring to Appendix Table IV, the z values are found in the left margin. Locate the z value of 1.0 and then read horizontally to the proportion given under .00. The proportion is 0. _____.

.3413

20 _____

Since the normal curve is symmetrical, what percent of the weights are between 90 ounces and 100 ounces? 0. _____.
What is the probability that if one of the ball bearings is selected at random it would weigh between 90 ounces and 110 ounces, i.e., between $\mu \pm 1\sigma$? 0. _6826_
_____. What is the probability that it will weigh between $\mu \pm 2\sigma$? _0.9544_
_____. Between $\mu \pm 3\sigma$? About 0. _9973_

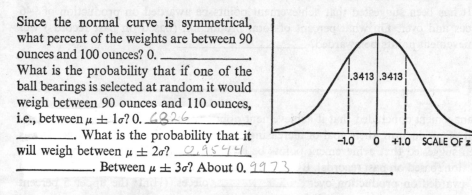

.3413

.6826, found by 0.3413 + 0.3413

.9544
.9973

21 _____

The mean μ divides the normal probability distribution into two equal parts with the proportion above the mean being 0. _____ and the area below the mean also being 0. _____. Note that the mean of the standardized normal distribution is zero and the standard deviation is 1. To find the proportion of ball bearings weighing more than 110 ounces, the proportion between 100 and 110 (0.3413) is subtracted from 0.5000. The proportion weighing more than 110 ounces is 0. _____
_____.

.5000
.5000

.1587

Shown schematically:

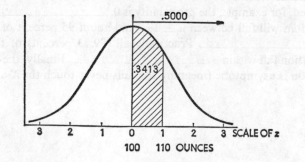

.6793, found by 0.1915 +
0.4878

22 _____

Using the same data (mean = 100 ounces, standard deviation = 10 ounces), what is the probability of selecting a ball bearing at random and finding that it weighed between 95 ounces and 122.5 ounces? 0. _____.

23 _____

0.0018 (less than 1 percent), found by:

$$z = \frac{946 - 800}{50} = 2.92$$

Then, 0.5000 − 0.4982 = 0.0018

Management is considering awarding achievement points for production over a specified number of pieces in order to increase production. Past records on the production of a small electronic component revealed that the distribution of production was somewhat normally distributed with a mean daily production per employee of 800 pieces and a standard deviation of 50 pieces. The electronic components are counted, and thus the data are considered discrete. However, the normal frequency curve, which was based on a large number of parts produced, allows a reasonable assumption to be made that the distribution is continuous.

It has been suggested that achievement points be awarded on production of 946 pieces and over. On what percent of total production (based on past records) will achievement points be awarded? _____.

24 _____

882.25 pieces, found by:

$$z = \frac{X - \mu}{\sigma};$$

$$1.645 = \frac{X - 800}{50}$$

Management concluded that if achievement points were awarded on less than 1 percent of production, their goal of increasing production would not be realized. It was then suggested that achievement points be awarded on the highest 5 percent of production (based on past records). If this plan went into effect, achievement points would be awarded on production over _____ pieces. (Hint: the upper 5 percent represents how many z values?)

25 _____

continuous

μ

σ

symmetrical

0

1

z value

.6826 (or 0.68)

2σ

3σ

In summary, the normal probability distribution is a (discrete/continuous) _____ distribution. It is described by a mean designated as _____, and a standard deviation designated as _____. The normal distribution is (skewed/symmetrical) _____ and appears as a smoothed curve. A *standardized* normal distribution has a mean of _____, and a standard deviation of _____. Using z, called the _____ probabilities can be determined for any normal distribution. It was noted, for example, the probability is 0. _____ that a value selected at random will fall between $\mu \pm 1\sigma$. And about 95 percent of the values fall between $\mu \pm$ _____. Practically all (99.73 percent) of the values in a normal distribution fall within $\mu \pm$ _____. Finally, the normal probability distribution is asymptotic (meaning the tails never touch the X-axis).

Final Self-Review Examination

First, answer all of the questions. Then check your answers against those given at the end of this chapter. Scoring: 10 problems × 10 points each = 100 possible points.

26. There are a large number of probability distributions. Of the three discussed in this chapter, which one(s) are discrete? (a)_____ _____. Which one(s) are continuous? (b)_____.

27. In order to construct any probability distribution, certain parameters (such as the mean) must be known. Which one(s) are needed to construct a:

    (a) binomial distribution_____
    _____
    _____.

    (b) Poisson distribution_____
    _____
    _____.

    (c) normal distribution_____
    _____
    _____.

28. A consumer research organization has an identification project. The sponsor of the project wants to know if grocery shoppers can identify the package of certain well-known foods (Campbell's soup, Lux soap, etc.). Ten different packages were selected and the names deleted. The sponsor has arbitrarily decided that consumers who are able to identify 8 or more packages out of 10 are *very brand conscious*, consumers who identify 5, 6, or 7 are *somewhat brand conscious*, and so on. The consumer research organization developed a questionnaire and pilot-tested the 10 unnamed packages on 100 consumers. Out of the 100 consumers, 30 identified 8, 9, or 10 correctly. The research firm is somewhat concerned that this group (30 percent of the total) might have just guessed the correct brand name and the results are really not significant. Is it highly possible that such a large percent could have guessed the brand name correctly? Explain your decision by citing evidence. _____
    _____

29. A high-speed shearing machine has been producing about 5 percent defective parts. What is the probability that if eight sheared pieces were selected at random none would be defective? _____

30. An analysis of past records revealed that about 10 percent of the total of a mass produced part were defective. That is, 10 percent of the parts contained a burr which had to be filed off. During the past hour, several samples of 10 parts were selected at random. Most of the samples contained four defective parts. Does it appear that something is wrong with the production process, or is it reasonable to expect 4 out of 10 in a sample to be defective? Give evidence. _____
    _____

31. A national grocery chain has made a large number of studies on the waiting lines at the checkout counters. They found there was an average of 1.0 shoppers waiting to be checked out. The distribution of waits appeared to follow the shape of the Poisson probability distribution. The management of the grocery customers chain has designed their checkout cash registers so that hardly ever will customers wait in a line of *four or more shoppers to check out*. Has management achieved its goal? Explain. _____
    _____

32. A trucking firm has found that on the average 2.0 of their earthmovers are inoperative on a given day. The distribution of the number of inoperative earthmovers follows a Poisson distribution. Out of 100 days, how many days will no earthmovers be inoperative? _____
    _____.

    Questions 33, 34, and 35 are based on the following problem.

    Supervisors and others have rated each management trainee on a scale of 0 to 150. The ratings for each trainee were combined into a composite rating, such as 95.34. Thus, the composite ratings can be considered as being continuous data. The distribution of all the ratings approximated a normal distribution with a mean rating of 100 and a standard deviation of 20.

33. Management wants a list of the names of the top 10 percent of the trainees. The trainees with a score of _____ or more would be on the list.

34. Management has decided to dismiss those with a score of less than 85. What percent of the trainees will be dismissed? _____.

35. Those between 85 and 105 will be given additional training before deciding on their fate. What percent of the trainees will get additional training? _____.

Answers to Final Self-Review Examination

26. (a) binomial, Poisson
    (b) normal

27. (a) p(the proportion defective) and n(number sampled)
    (b) the mean μ
    (c) the mean μ and the standard deviation σ

28. Highly improbable that 30 percent of consumers could guess 8, 9, or 10 brand names of products correctly. It seems then that 30 percent are "very brand conscious." To solve: Probability a consumer could guess the brand name of a package correctly is 0.50. $p = 0.50$; $n = 10$. Refer to Table VII. Add $0.0429 + 0.0098 + 0.0010 = 0.0547$. Only about 5 percent should have guessed 8, 9, or 10 brand names correctly. Thus 30 percent apparently can identify brand-name packages.

29. 0.6634

30. Something is wrong. Even if 10 percent of production were defective (a burr), only about 1 percent of the samples of size 10 should have contained a burr. (Refer to Table VII and $n = 10$, $p = .10$.) The probability is 0.0112 of selecting 4 out of 10 defective.

31. Yes. Only 1.8988 percent of the time should four or more persons be waiting to be checked out. Found by referring to Table VI, a μ of 1.0. Add $0.015328, 0.003066. \ldots 0.000001 = 0.018988$

32. 13.5335 days, found by referring to Table VI and reading the probability for a $\mu = 2.0$ and an X of 0. The probability is 0.135335.

33. 125.6, found by
    $$1.28 = \frac{X - 100}{20}$$
    To find the z of 1.28 find 0.4000 (Table IV)

34. 22.66 percent
    $z = -0.75$
    then, $0.5000 - 0.2734 = 0.2266$

35. 37.21 percent, found by $0.2734 + 0.0987$

An introduction to sampling

1 ────────────────────────────────────

Data needed to make decisions can be gathered by either studying all of the items in the population (a census), or selecting a few from the population for study (a sample). The fundamental purpose of sampling is to estimate a population value, called a population parameter, based on a sample value called a sample statistic. This estimation procedure is called *statistical inference*.

Suppose that a sample of 4,000 voters in the United States revealed that 3,200, or 80 percent, were in favor of reducing the voting age to 16 years. The sample value of 80 percent is called a _____. If the 80 percent were used to predict the outcome of a national vote on this issue, the procedure would be called _____.

sample statistic

statistical inference

2 ────────────────────────────────────

REASONS FOR SAMPLING

Checking each computer, each completed television set, and each automobile as it is manufactured is feasible. Contacting nearly 100 million voters one month prior to a national election in order to predict which candidate will win, or checking every fuse manufactured is not feasible. Thus, a sample is often employed because of the:

1. Destructive nature of some tests.
2. Prohibitive cost of examining the entire population.
3. Physical impossibility of studying all of the population, such as all of the fish in a lake.
4. Time limitation, such as imposed on political pollsters just prior to an election.
5. Adequacy of sample results. For example, an automotive manufacturer would probably be quite satisfied if a sample survey revealed that between 85 and 90 percent of the new car buyers would have installed an air conditioner if the price were a moderate $100.

METHODS OF PROBABILITY SAMPLING

It is essential that every item in the population has a chance of being chosen in the sample. Otherwise, the sample results might not be representative of the population. If this happens, the sample results are considered *biased*. Reasoning that they would be eminently qualified to speak for all consumers, a group of artists and designers in the Detroit, Michigan area were asked to rate certain styling features on the mock-up model of a proposed new automobile. Would this sample be biased? (yes/no) _____.
Why? _____

_____

yes
All consumers did not have a chance to express their opinions.

3 ────────────────────────────────────

One commonly used method of assuring that all items in the population have a known chance (probability) of being chosen in the sample is called *simple random sampling*, alternately called *probability sampling*. All draft-age males prior to World War II registered at a local draft board, and each was assigned a number. To assure that each male had an equal chance of being selected for service, the numbers were placed in a bowl. The Secretary of War began picking numbers from the bowl and men with those numbers were required to report to their draft board. This illustrates _____ _____ sampling.

simple random or probability sampling

4 _____

Since there were a known number of draft-age males, the population is considered a *finite* population. If the population is finite, instead of selecting numbers from a bowl a more convenient way of selecting the items to be sampled is by using a *table of random numbers*. For example, a sample from the 8,614 students at a university are to be surveyed. Each student has an identification number for payroll and other purposes starting with 0001 and ending with 8,614. The first few numbers from a table of random numbers are shown as follows.

0694	5965	7212	5888
9121	9791	5207	9769
6970	0319	7338	8785
3426	etc.	etc.	etc.

The numbers in this table are already randomized having been emitted by an IBM computer. Thus, student numbers can be chosen starting anywhere in the table called a _____. For illustration, the first number in the left column is 0694. The student with that identification number would be surveyed. Reading down the same column, 9,121 could not be used because there is no student with that identification number. The next student to be interviewed would have the identification number _____. Why was this method for randomly selecting students to interview followed? _____

table of random numbers

6,970
to prevent biased results, i.e., assure each student has a chance of being chosen

5 _____

A simple random sample may be awkward to select in certain cases. For example, if there were 1,000 invoices on file by date received to be audited on a sample basis, the invoices would have to be numbered from 0001 up to 1,000. Then a sample (say, 200 numbers) would have to be selected from a table of random numbers. The invoice to match each of the numbers would have to be located in the file.

Instead, a *systematic* sampling procedure may be used to audit the invoices. Thus, if there are 1,000 invoices and 200 are to be sampled, it may be more convenient, as well as more economical, to select every fifth invoice. The number of the first invoice should be selected using a random device such as a table of random numbers. If the number 4 were selected then the 4th, 9th, _____, and so on would be audited. The method described is called _____ sampling.

14th
systematic

6 _____

Systematic sampling should not be used if there is a predetermined pattern to the population. For example, it is desired to determine the average length of time an item stays in a warehouse. The warehouse is so arranged that the merchandise in the top bins are slow-moving items and the goods in the more accessible bins are the fast-moving items. Shown schematically:

4	8	12	16
3	7	11	15
2	6	10	14
1	5	9	13

TOP SHELVES (BINS) CONTAIN SLOW-MOVING ITEMS

LOWER SHELVES (BINS) CONTAIN FAST-MOVING ITEMS

If a systematic sample of every fourth bin were to be chosen starting with bin #4, then goods in bins _____, _____, and _____ would be checked. Thus, using a _____ type sample any inference based on the sample average would be biased because _____ _____.

#8, #12, and #16

systematic

only the slow-moving items would be chosen

7 _____

To correct the inadequacy of the systematic selection of bins, *stratified* sampling may be used. In the previous warehouse problem, the population is actually stratified into two *subpopulations*, or *strata*, i.e., slow-moving and fast-moving items. Each strata is sampled independently. If it were decided to use a *proportional* stratified sample in the same relationship as found in the population, then for every one slow-moving item sampled _____ fast-moving bins would be inventoried. When the items in the population are divided into subpopulations, or strata, such as in the warehouse problem, the sampling method is called _____ sampling.

3

stratified

8 _____

The number of items chosen in the sample need not be proportional to the proportion of items in the various strata. If the number chosen in each stratum is not proportional to their number in the subpopulations, the sampling method is called *nonproportional stratified sampling*. For example, a survey might involve interviewing presidents of firms in an industry. The firms were stratified according to the number of employees.

Size of Firm by Number of Employees	Number of Firms
Under 10	780
10 up to 100	210
100 and over	10
Total	1,000

If a proportional stratified sample of 100 firms were used, only (number) _____ president of a firm with 100 or more employees would be interviewed. However, the 10 large firms in the industry probably have sales in excess of the remaining 990 firms combined. Further, the one president interviewed might not be representative of the group. Therefore, it would be more desirable to survey more presidents of large firms (possibly all 10) and fewer medium-sized and small firms. This type of sampling would be designated as _____ _____ sampling. There are other probability methods (not discussed here).

1

nonproportional stratified

9

METHODS OF NONPROBABILITY SAMPLING

There is a significant amount of *nonprobability* sampling being done in the United States. The users of nonprobability sampling, such as firms engaged in determining the market potential of newly developed products, claim that it is less expensive, not so time-consuming, more convenient, and gives results as valid as those obtained from probability type sampling.

Judgment or *purposive* sampling is one type of nonprobability sampling. As the name implies, the selection of the items in the sample is left to the _____ of the researcher. A public opinion researcher with the problem of determining the preelection popularity of several candidates might select an area which in his judgment is typical of the voting population and concentrate his efforts in this area. This type of nonprobability sampling called _____ sampling generally reduces cost and can be completed in a relatively short period of time.

Convenience sampling is another type of nonprobability sampling. A nationally known bakery uses this type of sampling to test newly developed products. A small group of housewives are invited to taste and rate the pastry. Persons taking tours of automobile manufacturing plants in Detroit are often asked to rate the features of mockup models of proposed future automobiles.

Panel sampling is another nonprobability method of collecting quantitative data. Product testing firms such as National Family Opinion, Inc., and Market Facts, organize persons who have volunteered to test products or give opinions into panels. Each panel consists of about 2,000 persons. Dog owners would constitute one panel, families with children under 16 years might be another. The usual method of collecting the data is by mail questionnaire. The claimed advantages of this type of sampling are lower cost, a higher percent response because the participants are volunteers, and less time consumed because the respondents are always readily available.

(margin notes) judgment   judgment

Final Self-Review Examination

First, answer all of the questions. Then check your answers against those given at the end of this chapter. Scoring: 10 problems × 10 points each = 100 possible points.

10. The main purpose of sampling is to estimate a population (*a*)_____ based on a sample (*b*)_____.

11. Sampling, in contrast to a study of all items in the population, is often preferred because:
    (*a*) _____
    (*b*) _____
    (*c*) _____.

12. The two basic types of sampling are _____ and _____.

13. Three methods of probability sampling are _____, _____, _____, _____, _____.

14. Three methods of nonprobability sampling are _____, _____, _____, and _____.

15. Nonprobability sampling lacks one advantage of probability sampling; namely, _____ _____.

16. Selected families living contiguous to a proposed shopping center were interviewed. It was found that the mean income of the sample was $9,200. Based on a systematic sample, it was

noted in the written report that "if all the families in the area were surveyed the mean income would be between \$9,100 and \$9,300." A (probability/nonprobability) _____ _____ sample was used.

Identify the method of sampling in questions 17 through 19.

17. A manufacturer of cat food wanted to package a newly developed cat food in a clear container. In order to obtain consumer reaction, he hired a consumer opinion organization to do the research. Eight different forms of the food were mailed to 1,800 cat owners who had previously volunteered to test products and give opinions. Nearly 80 percent of the respondents thought that the food labeled "Ex-

hibit D" had the most appealing color and shape. This nonprobability sampling method is called _____ sampling.

18. Incoming orders are given a number and filed consecutively. Every tenth order was chosen in a sample starting with number 007 and continuing with 017, 027, 037, and so on. This method is called _____ sampling.

19. All union members have a card number. A table of random numbers was used to select numbers 1,395, 0024, 6,219, and so forth. Union members having those card numbers were surveyed regarding their political preferences. This method is called _____ _____ sampling.

Answers to Final Self-Review Examination

10. (a) parameter
    (b) statistic

11. (In any order) destructive nature of some tests, cost, less time consuming, adequacy of sample results, and the impossibility of studying all of the items in the population.

12. (Any order) probability, nonprobability

13. (Any order) simple random, systematic, stratified

14. (Any order) judgment, convenience, panel

15. (Any order) Using nonprobability sampling the items selected for study might not be representative of the population. Thus, the sample results might be biased.

16. probability

17. panel

18. systematic

19. simple random or probability

An introduction to statistical inference

1 _____

The purpose of sampling is to draw a conclusion about some measure of the population (called a *parameter*) based on a sample value (called a sample *statistic*). It was noted that a population might be composed of people or inanimate objects, such as automobile mufflers, nails, or television sets. An example of a marketing research problem might be to draw a conclusion about the arithmetic mean income of families living contiguous to a proposed new shopping center. Suppose that a random sample of 822 families in the area were interviewed and the arithmetic mean family income computed to be $9,200. The $9,200 is called a _____ _____.

sample statistic

2 _____

If one value is to be estimated, the specific estimate (such as $9,200) is called a *point estimate*. Thus, based on the sample of 822 families, this point estimate is the best estimate of the population mean obtainable. It should be realized that the sample statistic of $9,200, called a _____ estimate, may not be exactly the same as the population mean. Therefore, it may be desirable to specify a range or interval, within which the population mean might fall. For example, based on the sample mean of $9,200, the *confidence limits* might be calculated to be $9,100 and $9,300. (The necessary calculations will be examined shortly.) A probability, such as 0.90, is attached to these two numbers. It is then inferred with a probability of 0.90 that the mean income of *all* families in the proposed shopping area is in the interval from $9,100 to $9,300.

point

3 _____

INFERENCES INVOLVING MEANS

A concept essential to the understanding of statistical inference is called the *sampling distribution of the mean*. To illustrate, suppose that the incomes of *all* the families in the proposed shopping center area were known. The incomes were organized into a frequency distribution and plotted as a frequency polygon (Figure A). Is the population distribution (normal/positively skewed/negatively skewed)? _____

positively skewed

FIGURE A

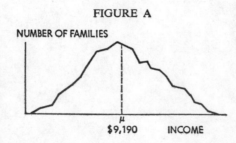

NUMBER OF FAMILIES

$9,190   INCOME

μ

A sample of 100 families were selected at random from the population and their annual incomes organized into a frequency distribution and plotted in Figure B. Another sample of 100 families (designated as Sample #2) is also plotted in Figure B. A comparison of the population distribution and sample distributions reveals (1) that the distribution of sample values tend to follow the same shape as the population values, i.e., the two sample distributions are also _____ _____ skewed. Make two other observations about the sample distributions (Figure B).

_____
_____
_____
_____
_____
_____
_____

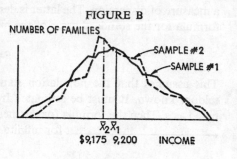

FIGURE B

NUMBER OF FAMILIES

SAMPLE #2
SAMPLE #1

$\bar{X}_2\ \bar{X}_1$
$9,175\ 9,200$ INCOME

FIGURE C

NUMBER OF MEANS

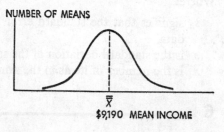

$\bar{\bar{X}}$
$9,190$ MEAN INCOME

positively
(In any order.) The actual distributions of the two samples are different and the means are different.

4

The central-limit theorem

If the mean incomes of all possible samples of size 100 were plotted, the distribution of these sample means would approximate a *normal probability distribution* (Figure C in the previous illustration). Thus, if the distribution of the population values is skewed, the distributions of the sample values selected from that population will tend to be _____. However, the distribution of a large number of the sample means will tend to be _____ distributed. This distribution is called the *sampling distribution of the mean*. This concept is part of the *central-limit theorem*. A statement of the theorem is: *If a large number of random samples are chosen from any population (either normal or skewed), the means of these samples will approximate a normal probability distribution. And, the mean of these sample means (written $\bar{\bar{X}}$) will approach the population mean (written μ).*

skewed
normally

5

The standard error of the mean

The importance of the central-limit theorem will now be examined. In "real-world" sampling problems it is not feasible to take thousands of samples of, say, size 100 just to estimate the population mean. The cost and time limitations usually restrict the researcher to selecting *one* sample from the population. On the basis of this one sample he can make a point estimate and give the _____ limits for the population mean.

The confidence limits for the mean are based on a measure of central tendency and

confidence

a measure of dispersion. The latter is designated as the *standard error of the mean*. The formula for the standard error of the mean is:

$$\sigma_{\bar{x}} = \frac{\sigma}{\sqrt{n}}$$

This assumes that the population standard deviation (σ) is known. However, σ is seldom known. It must be estimated by using the sample standard deviation, designated as s. Then the formula for the measure called the _____

standard error of the mean

_____ for infinite populations becomes:

$$s_{\bar{x}} = \frac{s}{\sqrt{n}}$$

Where:

$s_{\bar{x}}$ signifies that the standard error of the mean is being estimated using sample data.

s is the standard deviation of the sample.

n is the number of items in the sample.

6 ──

To illustrate its computation, suppose that the mean tensile strength of an infinite number of steel wires is to be evaluated by selecting a random sample of 100 wires from the population and breaking them. Each wire was tested and the tensile strength recorded. The standard deviation of the sample was computed to be 500 pounds per square inch (written psi). Show the formula and compute the standard error of the mean.

$$s_{\bar{x}} = \frac{s}{\sqrt{n}} = \frac{500}{\sqrt{100}} = 50 \text{ psi}$$

$s_{\bar{x}} = \underline{\hspace{1cm}} = \underline{\hspace{1cm}} = \underline{\hspace{1cm}}$ psi

7 ──

The confidence interval and confidence limits

The arithmetic mean tensile strength of the 100 sample pieces was computed to be 10,000 psi. Obviously, all of the wires cannot be broken to determine the population mean (μ). The mean of the sample ($\bar{x}$) and the standard error of the mean ($s_{\bar{x}}$) are combined to set up the *confidence interval* for the population mean. In order to determine the confidence interval it is necessary to determine the two confidence limits of the sample mean. The 95 percent confidence limits (also stated as the 0.95 confidence limits) are computed by $\bar{x} \pm z s_{\bar{x}} = \bar{x} \pm 1.96 s_{\bar{x}}$

Give the formula for the 95 percent confidence limits for the sample mean for the tensile strength problem, insert the appropriate numbers and solve. The 0.95 confidence limits = _____ = _____ = _____ and _____ psi.

$\bar{x} \pm 1.96 s_{\bar{x}}$
$= 10,000 \pm 1.96(50)$
$= 9,902$ and $10,098$ psi

8 ──

about 9,883.5 psi and 10-, 116.5, found by 10,000 $\pm$ 2.33(50)

What are the 0.98 confidence limits for the same problem involving the tensile strengths of the steel wires? _____ psi and _____ psi. (If needed, refer to Chapter 7 frame #19 for a review of the procedure for determining the appro-

priate z value.) Now interpret what these two confidence limits indicate. _____
_____.

What is the probability that the population mean tensile strength is not in the interval between 9,883.5 psi and 10,116.5 psi? _____.

9

Finite populations

The formula $s/\sqrt{n}$ is applied to infinitely large populations. It is also applicable if the sampling is done with replacement (meaning that the item drawn at random is put back in the population before another selection is made). In effect, sampling with replacement is the same as an infinitely large population.

A modification is made to the formula for the standard error of the mean when the population is *finite* and the sample size is a large proportion of the total population. Recall that a finite population means that the total number of persons (or inanimate objects) are known. The modification is called the *finite population correction factor* and is often referred to as the *finite multiplier*. The finite correction factor is:

$$\sqrt{\frac{N - n}{N - 1}}$$

Where:

N is the size of the population.

n is the size of the sample.

Applying this correction factor, the standard error of the mean for a _____ population is:

finite

$$s_{\bar{x}} = \frac{s}{\sqrt{n}} \sqrt{\frac{N - n}{N - 1}}$$

Suppose that there were 1,500 members of a union and 200 were selected at random. The correction factor is _____.

0.931

10

The finite correction factor, therefore, compensates for the size of the sample in relation to the size of the population. To illustrate this further, note in the following table that the correction factor is approximately 0.997 if only 9 members out of 1,500 members of the union (about 1 percent) were sampled. This is logical. The error in estimating the mean wage of the population of 1,500 based on a sample of 1,000 (67 percent of the population) should be less than the error in estimating the mean wage based only on nine members.

Size of Sample	Size of Finite Population	Size of Sample Size of Population (Percent)	Correction Factor
9	1,500	0.6	0.997
50	1,500	3.3	.983
200	1,500	13.3	.931
1,000	1,500	66.7	.619
1,500	1,500	100.0	0

Some statisticians do not apply the correction factor unless the size of the sample is at least 5 percent of the size of the population, and others disregard it until the sample size is at least 10 percent of the total.

In review, suppose that there are 2,001 executives in the aircraft industry. A random sample of 400 were given a test on the principles of management. The mean test score was computed to be 180 and the standard deviation of the scores found to be 60. With probability of 0.95, the mean test score of the population is in the interval between _____ and _____. Show the formula and essential work.

approximately 174.74 and 185.26 found by,

$$180 \pm 1.96 \frac{60}{\sqrt{400}} \sqrt{\frac{2{,}001 - 400}{2{,}001 - 1}}$$

Estimating the population mean for small samples

The previous frames dealt with large samples selected at random from a population. If the sample size is small, the confidence limits are determined by $\bar{x} + t(s_{\bar{x}})$. Note that the only difference when working with a small sample is that a t-multiple is used instead of a z-multiple. The concept of the t-multiple was developed by W. S. Gosset, an Irish brewmaster, writing under the name of Student. In brief, he developed a set of t-multiples for each sample size. These distributions are commonly referred to as *Student t* distributions (not considered here).

11

INFERENCES INVOLVING PROPORTIONS

The procedure for determining the confidence interval for the population proportion is quite similar to that developed for a variable examined in the previous frames. To illustrate, suppose a random sample of 1,000 students revealed that 800 liked a revolutionary new writing pen. The point estimate of the population proportion is 0.80 found by:

$$\bar{p} = \frac{x}{n} = \frac{800}{1{,}000}$$

where x is the number in favor of the pen and n is the sample size. To find the confidence limits for the population proportion:

$$\bar{p} \pm z s_{\bar{p}}$$

The standard error of the proportion ($s_{\bar{p}}$) is computed by:

For infinite populations	For finite populations
$s_{\bar{p}} = \sqrt{\dfrac{\bar{p}(1 - \bar{p})}{n}}$	$s_{\bar{p}} = \sqrt{\dfrac{N - n}{N - 1}} \sqrt{\dfrac{\bar{p}(1 - \bar{p})}{n}}$

Assuming that the student population is infinite, construct the 0.95 confidence limits for the proportion of the student population who would like the revolutionary new pen. Show essential formulas and work in the space provided. Give answers to the nearest 10th of a percent, such as 89.4 percent. _____ and _____ percent.

77.5 and 82.5, found by

$$0.80 \pm 1.96 \sqrt{\frac{0.80(1 - 0.80)}{1{,}000}}$$

12

Sample size involving variables

A development company is considering building a shopping mall. One of the figures needed is the mean income of the residents. It would be too expensive and time-consuming to survey all residents in the area. One might ask, "How many residents should be included in a sample? 3? 50? 500? 8,000?"

Several factors have an influence on the size of the sample. The management of the development company no doubt has some idea of the precision required in the estimate of the population mean. For example, management might want the estimate of the population mean to be within $100. This would indicate that *if* the sample mean was computed to be $10,000, it would be stated that the population mean is in the interval between _____ and _____.

$9,900 and $10,100, found by $10,000 ± $100

13 _____

A second factor in determining the size of the sample is the confidence coefficient. If the 0.95 confidence coefficient were selected, management would be 95 percent confident that the interval between $9,900 and $10,100 contains the population mean.

The third factor needed is an estimate of the standard deviation of the population. This can be estimated from experience, or by taking a pilot sample of, say, 30 persons. Suppose the pilot survey revealed that the standard deviation of the population is approximately $1,000. Management has specified that the sample be of sufficient size to include the population mean in the interval of ±$100 from the sample mean. Using the 0.95 confidence coefficient (and rounding 1.96 to 2 to simplify calculations), the confidence limits for the population mean are computed by:

$$\bar{x} \pm 2(s_{\bar{x}}) \quad \text{or} \quad \bar{x} \pm 2\left(\frac{s}{\sqrt{n}}\right)$$

In effect, management specified that the population mean must fall in the interval of $2s_{\bar{x}}$ or 2 ($100). Thus $s_{\bar{x}} = $50, found by $100/2. This concept is shown schematically.

Substituting the $50 standard error specified by management and the estimated standard deviation of $1,000 from the pilot survey:

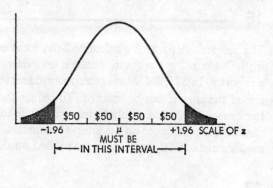

DISTRIBUTION OF SAMPLE MEANS OF SIZE *n*

$50 | $50 | $50 | $50

−1.96   μ   +1.96 SCALE OF z
          MUST BE
|——— IN THIS INTERVAL ———|

$$\$50 = \frac{\$1,000}{\sqrt{n}}$$

Solve for the size of the sample. *n* = _____.

400

14 _____

The sample size of 400 might not give the precision demanded by management (an estimate of the population mean within $100) because the population standard deviation might not be $1,000. (The $1,000 was determined from a very small pilot survey of 30 persons.) The sample of 400 persons might yield a confidence interval that is too large, too small, or exactly correct.

Suppose that the sample of 400 resulted in a sample standard deviation of $1,250. What should have been the sample size? _____. Was the initial sample of 400 too (small/large)? _____

625, found by $50 = $\dfrac{\$1,250}{\sqrt{n}}$

small, additional (225) persons must be surveyed

15

Sample size involving proportions

The procedures for estimating the sample size for problems involving proportions and variables are quite similar: (1) management must specify how precise the estimate of the population proportion is to be, (2) a confidence coefficient must be selected, and (3) the standard error of the proportion ($s_{\bar{p}}$) can be approximated from experience, or by taking a small pilot survey.

To illustrate, suppose that management wants to estimate the population proportion of homeowners in the metropolitan area who apply crabgrass killer to their lawns in the spring and fall. Management wants the estimate to be within an interval of ± 2 percent of the sample proportion. Also, the 0.98 confidence coefficient is to be used. A previous survey by the company in another metropolitan area resulted in a point estimate of the population proportion of 0.20. These three factors can be combined to determine the sample size (n). Recall that the standard error of the proportion is found by:

$$s_{\bar{p}} = \sqrt{\frac{\bar{p}(1 - \bar{p})}{n}}$$

Substituting the three known values:

Specified by management → 0.02
The z-multiple for 0.98 ⟶ 2.33

$$\frac{0.02}{2.33} = \sqrt{\frac{0.20(1 - 0.20)}{n}} \begin{array}{l} \leftarrow \text{From a previous sample} \\ \leftarrow\!\!\!- \text{Unknown} \end{array}$$

Solve for the size of the sample $n = $ _____ homeowners.

about 2,172, found by

$$\frac{0.02}{2.33} = \frac{\sqrt{0.16}}{\sqrt{n}}$$

$$0.02\sqrt{n} = 2.33\sqrt{.16}$$

$$n = (46.6)^2$$

16

The research department calculated the total cost of surveying 2,172 homeowners, including printing the questionnaires, interviewing, tabulating the results, and writing a report to be $15,204. Management considers this cost to be excessive and asks if the size of the sample can be reduced. To reduce the size of the sample, one possibility is to change the confidence coefficient from 0.98 to, say, 0.95. In effect, this would place slightly less confidence on the interval estimates. If the 0.95 confidence coefficient were used instead of 0.98, the sample size needed would be _____.

about 1,600 if the rounded z-multiple of 2 is used; 1,537 if 1.96 is used.

Work: using $z = 2$:

$$\frac{0.02}{2} = \sqrt{\frac{0.20(1 - 0.20)}{u}}$$

$$0.02\sqrt{n} = 2\sqrt{.16}$$

$$n = (40)^2$$

17

The cost using the 0.95 confidence coefficient was found to be $11,200. Suppose that management wants to cut the cost even further, but retain the 0.95 confidence coefficient. What other concession can management make to affect a reduction in the size of the sample? (Hint: They want the population proportion to be estimated within the interval of ± 0.02 of the sample proportion.) _____
_____.

Increase the size of the interval to, say, ±0.04.

18

Management indicated that it would be satisfactory if it were estimated that the population proportion was within ± 0.04 of the sample proportion. Now, using this revised precision figure ($\pm$ 0.04), the confidence coefficient selected (0.95), and the proportion of homeowners found in another survey (0.20), determine the sample size. _____ _____. Show work.

400 if z-multiple is rounded to 2; 384 if 1.96 is used.

$$\frac{0.04}{2} = \sqrt{\frac{0.16}{n}}$$

$$n = (20)^2$$

This number (400) would only cost $2,800 to survey. Again, because the population proportion was estimated to be 20 percent (a previous survey) the sample size might be too large or too small. Thus, the size of the sample is often a compromise between the cost of taking the sample and the preciseness desired by management.

Final Self-Review Examination

First, answer all of the questions. Then check your answers against those given at the end of this chapter. Scoring 10 problems $\times$ 10 points each = 100 possible points.

19. Explain what is meant by statistical inference. _____ _____ _____

20. In connection with sampling, explain each of the following words:
    statistic   (a)_____.
    parameter (b)_____.
    population (c)_____.

21. State the general concept of the central-limit theorem. _____ _____ _____

22. It was found that the arithmetic mean weight of 100 items selected at random was 11,500 pounds. With a probability of 0.95, it was estimated that the population mean is between 11,400 pounds and 11,600 pounds. These two values (11,400 and 11,700) are called _____.

23. A sample of 400 executives were chosen at random and the mean age of the group computed to be 50 years. The standard deviation of the sample is 8 years. The 98 percent confidence limits for the population mean are (a) _____ and _____ years. Explain what the figures indicate. (b) _____ _____

24. A total of 1,001 new parts were produced on the first production run. A sample of 100 revealed that the mean inside diameter is 2.0000 inches. The standard deviation of the sample was computed to be 0.0002 inches. The 0.92 confidence limits for the population mean are _____ and _____ inches. (Note that the population is finite.)

25. A small sample of 18 pieces of wire were selected at random and the mean tensile strength computed to be 10,000 pounds per square inch. The standard error of the mean was found to be 10 psi. The 90 percent confidence limits for the population mean are _____ psi and _____ psi.

26. A sample public opinion poll revealed that 600 were in favor of the proposed amendment and 400 were against it. Construct the 95 percent confidence limits for the proportion of the total population in favor of the amendment. _____ and _____

27. The manufacturer of a foreign car is studying the possibility of introducing a new warranty. One figure needed is the arithmetic mean mileage on the odometer of their five-year-old cars. To collect this information for all cars would be expensive and time-consuming. Thus, the number to be sampled is important. Management wants to use the 0.95 confidence coefficient, and estimate the population mean within 1,000 miles. A very small pilot survey of the five-year-old cars indicated that the mean will probably be about 50,000 miles. The standard

deviation of the pilot survey was computed to be 10,000 miles. How many should be sampled? (a)_____. If the sample size computed for answer (a) is considered too large, what specifically could be done to reduce the size of the sample? Management could either (b)_____ or _____ (or do both).

28. One large voting precinct has been tradition-

ally Republican. The vote is usually 90 percent Republican. A pre-election poll is to be conducted to determine if there has been any change in the voting preference. The 0.95 confidence coefficient is to be used in determining the sample size and the population proportion is to be within an interval of plus and minus 3 percent of the sample proportion. What sample size is needed? _____.

Answers to Final Self-Review Examination

19. Statistical inference is a procedure which has been developed to describe a characteristic of a population (such as the mean income of typists) based on a sample selected from that population.

20. (a) A statistic refers to a sample value, such as mean of the sample is 81 pounds.
(b) A parameter refers to a population value, such as the median income of all persons in the United States is $8,710.
(c) A population refers to the total of either persons or inanimate objects. For example, the population might be defined as all of the students in the freshman English course at Sociable University, or all the light bulbs produced during the past month in the Schenectady plant.

21. The central-limits theorem states that (1) if a large number of random samples are selected from the population, the distribution of the sample means will approximate a normal probability distribution, (2) the mean of the sample means will approximate the population mean, and (3) the standard error of the mean of the sampling distribution is equal to $\sigma/\sqrt{n}$.

22. confidence limits

23. about 49.068 and 50.932 years, found by

$$50 \pm 2.33 \left(\frac{8}{\sqrt{400}} \right)$$

The statistician is 98 percent confident that the population mean is in the interval between 49.068 and 50.932 years.

24. approximately 1.999967 inches and 2.000033 inches, found by

$$2.0000 \pm 1.75 \frac{.0002}{\sqrt{100}} \sqrt{\frac{1,001 - 100}{1,001 - 1}}$$

25. 9,982.6 and 10,017.4 psi, found by $10,000 \pm 1.740 (10)$

26. about 0.57 and 0.63, found by

$$0.60 \pm 1.96 \sqrt{\frac{0.60(1 - 0.60)}{1,000}}$$

27. (a) approximately 400, found by
$$\frac{1,000}{2} = \frac{10,000}{\sqrt{n}}$$
(b) The confidence coefficient could be reduced from 0.95 to say 0.90 and/or the allowable error could be increased from 1,000 miles to, say, 1,500 miles.

28. about 400, found by
$$\frac{0.03}{2} = \sqrt{\frac{0.90(1 - 0.90)}{n}}$$

Statistical decision theory: tests of hypotheses

1

In this chapter, decision-making processes will be discussed regarding two means and two proportions. Two typical problems might be: Based on a sample of wire submitted by two suppliers, is the mean tensile strength of the wire of one company significantly higher than the mean tensile strength of the wire of the other company—or is it quite probable that the difference is due to sampling? A sample of residents living on the East Side revealed that 80 percent were in favor of Amendment No. 1, but on the West Side only 60 percent were in favor of it. One might ask, is it highly likely the difference in percents is due to sampling? Other problems might involve the difference between the mean income of two groups, or the difference between the proportion of men and women who like a new styling feature of a new automobile.

THE DECISION PROCEDURE

The decision procedure is alternatively called *rules of decision, tests of hypotheses,* or *tests of significance.* Six steps are usually followed in arriving at a decision.

1. State the hypothesis to be tested as well as the alternative hypothesis.
2. Select a level of significance.
3. Decide on an appropriate statistical test, examine the underlying theory and state the statistic needed.
4. Define the region of acceptance and the region of rejection.
5. Choose a random sample and compute the essential sample statistics.
6. Accept or reject the hypothesis at the level of significance selected.

Each of the six steps will now be discussed in detail.

The null hypothesis

A contractor needs a steel wire which will be woven into a cable for a bridge span. The wire must test at least 7,500 pounds per square inch (psi), or it will not be considered. Two companies, the Strongwire Company and Federal Steel, plan to submit samples for testing. First, however, a hypothesis is stated primarily to either *accept* it or to *reject* it. The hypothesis can be stated either positively or negatively. In this chapter, it has been arbitrarily decided to state it negatively, i.e., as a *null* hypothesis.

The contractor decided that if the two companies submit a sample of wires which test over 7,500 psi one of two actions will be taken—either to award the contract to one company, or to divide the contract equally between Strongwire and Federal. A general statement of the null hypothesis is that the two population means are equal; i.e., there is *no significant difference* between μ_1 and μ_2. *Thus, if this is true, any difference between the two sample means is merely due to sampling (chance).*

State the null hypothesis concerning the wire to be used for the bridge span. _____

_____

"There is no significant difference between the mean of the wires from the Strongwire Company and the mean of the Federal wires."

The contractor plans to divide the contract equally if there is no significant difference between the two mean tensile strengths of the samples. If there is significant difference between the two mean tensile strengths, the contract for the wires will be given to the company submitting the stronger wires.

If the null hypothesis is *accepted* (based on the samples submitted), the contract

divided equally

will be (divided equally/given to one company) _____

_____. If the null hypothesis is *rejected*, the difference between the two means

is

(is/is not) _____ significant. If the null hypothesis is *accepted*,

could

the difference between the two means (could/could not) _____ be due to sampling (chance).

2

The level of significance

Three of the most commonly used levels of significance are the 0.10 level, the 0.05 level, and the 0.01 level. The 0.05 level of significance was selected for this problem. There is a 5 percent chance that the statistician will reject the null hypothesis when he should have accepted it. This is called a *Type I error*. If the null hypothesis were rejected in this tensile strength problem, explain what the level of significance indicates. "The level of significance in this problem is the probability that—_____

_____

_____

_____."

the null hypothesis should have been accepted instead of being rejected. (This indicates that *if* in reality the two population mean tensile strengths were equal, the probability that a Type I error was made in rejecting the null hypothesis and giving the contract to just one company is 0.05.)

3

The test, the theory, and the statistic needed

In order to explain the theory underlying the ultimate decision, assume that two populations are identical. A sample is selected from one of the populations and the mean and the standard deviation of the sample are computed. Then a sample from the other population is selected, and the same two sample statistics are determined. Using these two sets of sample statistics, a measure called the *critical ratio* (designated as z) is determined. The statistic z is computed by:

$$z = \frac{\bar{X}_1 - \bar{X}_2}{\sqrt{\left(\frac{s_1}{\sqrt{n_1}}\right)^2 + \left(\frac{s_2}{\sqrt{n_2}}\right)^2}}$$

Suppose this procedure was repeated a large number of times. The sampling theory states that the large number of critical ratios which were computed will be normally distributed about a mean of 0. To put it another way, if all the critical ratios resulting

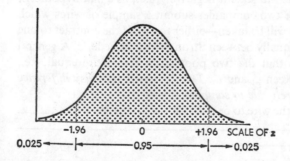

from a large number of samples taken from the two populations were plotted (assuming that there is no difference between the two populations), they would approximate a normal curve. The mean of the z values would be zero. About 95 percent of the critical ratios would fall between 0 and ±1.96.

The region of acceptance and the region of rejection

Now a *decision rule* will be formulated. If a random sample is taken from the wires of the Strongwire Company and another random sample is selected from the wires submitted by Federal Steel and the z value computed, the null hypothesis will be *accepted* at the 0.05 level if the computed z falls between 0 and +1.96, or 0 and −1.96. The null hypothesis will be *rejected* at the 0.05 level of significance if the computed z value does not fall in the area between +1.96 and −1.96. That is, if the computed z value is 1.96 or greater, the null hypothesis is rejected. The two areas beyond +1.96 and −1.96 are called the *tails* of the curve. This diagram shows the two regions.

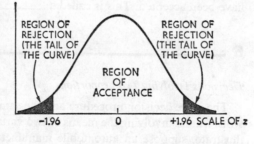

REGION OF REJECTION (THE TAIL OF THE CURVE) REGION OF REJECTION (THE TAIL OF THE CURVE)

REGION OF ACCEPTANCE

−1.96   0   +1.96 SCALE OF z

Suppose the two samples were selected and the critical ratio z was computed to be +0.82. The null hypothesis would be (accepted/rejected) _____ at the 0.05 level of significance (previously selected). If this did happen, how would the contract for the wires be awarded? (divided equally/awarded to company with the higher sample mean tensile strength) _____
_____. Thus, the difference between the two sample means (could/could not) _____ be due to chance.

It should be noted that this is a *two-tailed test* because there is a possibility that the sign of z may be either positive or negative. If the sign of z can only be positive, or it can only be negative, it is called a one-tailed test.

accepted

divide contract equally

could

4

The samples and the sample results

A sample (n) of 64 pieces of wire were selected at random from the wires of the Strongwire Company and each tested for tensile strength. A sample of 100 wires were selected from the wires of Federal Steel. The mean ($\bar{X}$) and the standard deviation (s) of each were computed. The results were:

Strongwire Company	Federal Steel
$\bar{X}_1 = 8{,}500$ psi	$\bar{X}_2 = 8{,}000$ psi
$s_1 = 120$ psi	$s_2 = 200$ psi
$n_1 = 64$	$n_2 = 100$

Determine the critical ratio:

$$z = \frac{\bar{X}_1 - \bar{X}_2}{\sqrt{\left(\frac{s_1}{\sqrt{n_1}}\right)^2 + \left(\frac{s_2}{\sqrt{n_2}}\right)^2}} = \underline{\hspace{1cm}} = \sqrt{\underline{\hspace{1cm}}} =$$

$z = +20$, found by $500/\sqrt{625}$

5

The decision

In this case, the null hypothesis is (accepted/rejected) _____ because +20 falls _____. It is highly un-

rejected
in the tail, i.e., it is greater than +1.96

likely that the difference of 500 psi could be due to _____.
How should the contract be awarded? _____
_____. Why? _____
_____.

The probability is 0.05 that the null hypothesis has been rejected when it should have been accepted. This is called a _____ error.

6 _____

Decisions involving two proportions

The same decision procedure and the same sampling theory examined in the previous frames involving the means of two variables is applicable to two proportions. To illustrate, suppose an automobile manufacturer built a mock model of a proposed new automobile. One of his problems is to find out whether it appeals equally to persons under 25 years and persons over 25 years of age.
State the null hypothesis. _____

The level of significance was arbitrarily selected as 0.01. Give the statistic needed. The statistic needed is called the _____, and is designated by the letter _____.

7 _____

The decision rule. Recall that the level of significance is 0.01. The dividing point between the region of acceptance and the region of rejection is 2.575. To find this number, refer to Appendix Table IV and search for 0.4950 (which is half of 0.9900). The decision rule is: If the computed z falls between ± 2.575, the null hypothesis will be _____. If the computed z is ± 2.575 or greater, the null hypothesis will be _____. This is a (one-tailed/two-tailed) _____ test because _____.

8 _____

The sample and sample results. Out of 2,000 younger men (under 25 years) sampled, 1,600 or 80 percent were enthusiastic about the new car design. Out of 1,000 older men (over 25 years) sampled, 821 or 82.1 percent were enthusiastic about it. The basic question is whether the difference of 2.1 percent ($0.80 - 0.821$) is significant, or whether this difference could be due to sampling. To compute the critical ratio:

$$z = \frac{p_1 - p_2}{\sqrt{\dfrac{\bar{P}(1 - \bar{P})}{n_1} + \dfrac{\bar{P}(1 - \bar{P})}{n_2}}}$$

Where:
p_1 is the sample proportion of younger men
p_2 is the sample proportion of older men.
n_1 is the total number of younger men sampled

Left margin answer column:

chance, or sampling
Strongwire Company
95 percent certain that the
wires of Strongwire have
a higher tensile strength.
Type I

There is no difference between the proportion of young persons and the proportion of older persons in favor of the proposed car design.
critical ratio
z

accepted
rejected   two-tailed
The critical ratio may be
either positive or negative.

n_2 is the total number of older men sampled.
$\bar{P}$ is the weighted proportion found by

$$\frac{X_1 + X_2}{n_1 + n_2}$$

X_1 is the number of younger men enthusiastic about the car
X_2 is the number of older men enthusiastic about it.

Insert the appropriate figures in the formula and solve for the critical ratio. The critical ratio is _____.

9

The decision. The null hypothesis should be _____ at the _____ _____ level of significance. The difference of 2.1 percent (is/is not) _____ _____ significant. It is highly likely that the difference between the two proportions (is/is not) _____ due to sampling (chance). Thus, if all the young men in the United States and all the older men in the United States viewed the mock model of the automobile, and the proportion of each group who were enthusiastic about it were computed, the two population proportions would probably be (equal/unequal) _____.

10

Tests of hypotheses involving a known population mean and variance

Records have been kept by an airline on the length of life of an electronic part. It was found that the arithmetic mean length of life of the part was 200,000 miles and the standard deviation 10,000 miles. All the parts have been supplied by one manufacturer, and the airline has been satisfied with the price, delivery, and service. The Longlasting Manufacturing Company, however, claims that they have perfected the same electronic part, and its average length of life is significantly longer.

The null hypothesis is $\mu = 200,000$ miles, which is the same as saying that the average length of life ($\bar{X}$) of the Longlasting Company parts is not significantly different from the mean length of life determined from the long experience of the airlines with this electronic part. The level of significance chosen is 0.05. The statistic z is needed. The critical ratio z is found by:

$$z = \frac{\bar{X} - \mu}{\dfrac{\sigma}{\sqrt{n}}}$$

This is a one-tail test because there is only an interest in testing whether the electronic parts from Longlasting are superior, i.e., Is the mean length of life significantly more than the population mean of 200,000 miles? There would be no problem if the parts from Longlasting had a mean life-span of less than 200,000. (The airline would continue buying from the present supplier.) Thus, the critical value for the decision rule is 1.645 (instead of 1.96), found by finding the critical value for 0.4500 in Appendix Table IV. Shown schematically:

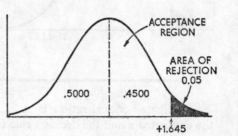

---

about $-1.4(-1.374)$, found by

$$\bar{P} = \frac{1,600 + 821}{2,000 + 1,000}$$

$$\frac{0.80 - 0.821}{\sqrt{\dfrac{0.807(1 - 0.807)}{2,000} + \dfrac{0.807(1 - 0.807)}{1,000}}}$$

accepted
0.01
is not
is

equal

accepted

Thus, the decision rule states that if the computed critical ratio z is less than +1.645 the null hypothesis should be (accepted/rejected) _____.

A sample of 2,500 parts were selected from the production line of Longlasting Manufacturing and the parts tested under an accelerated life testing program. The mean life was 215,000 miles. (The dispersion about the mean was quite satisfactory.) The question is, could this large a difference between the population mean (200,000 miles) and this sample mean be due to chance (sampling)? Find the critical ratio z _____.

+75, found by 15,000/200
rejected
no
Price and other factors being equal, buy from Longlasting. Their electronic parts do last longer on the average.

5

At the 0.05 level of significance the null hypothesis is _____. Is it likely that the difference between the two means is due to chance? (yes/no) _____ Recommend a course of action for the airline. _____.

There is a _____ percent chance that the hypothesis has been rejected when it should have been accepted.

11

Tests of hypothesis involving a known population proportion

The difference between the sample proportion and the known population proportion is not significant.

The soup company only has a problem when the sample proportion is less than the population percent of 0.40.

Past records of a soup company reveal that 40 percent of the test group must indicate a newly developed soup is excellent or the soup will not be successful (if marketed). A new soup called "Beefy" is given the usual testing, and 600 out of the 2,000 sampled, or 30 percent, rated it excellent. One might ask, could this large a difference (0.10, found by 0.40 − 0.30) be due to sampling? The null hypothesis to be tested is _____. The level of significance selected is 0.01.

This is a one-tail test. Why? _____.

The critical ratio z is computed by:

$$z = \frac{p - P}{\sqrt{\frac{P(1 - P)}{n}}}$$

where small letter p is the sample proportion, capital P is the known population proportion, and n is the number in the sample.

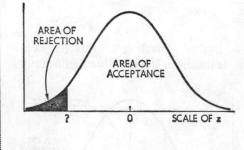

−2.33

−2.33

The decision rule is shown schematically. Thus, the decision rule is: accept the null hypothesis if the computed critical ratio z falls in the area to the right of _____, but reject it if z falls in the tail of the normal curve i.e., _____ or beyond.

12

about −9.1, found by −.10/√.00012

The computed critical ratio z is _____. Based on the value of the computed z and the decision rule formulated in the previous frame, make a deci-

sion and explain what it indicates. _____
_____
_____
_____.

13

Type I and Type II errors

In sampling, there is always a risk that a wrong decision has been made. The alpha risk, or the Type I error, is usually specified before the sampling is done. The probability of making a Type I error corresponds to the area in the tails of a normal curve. These areas are designated as the area of _____. The Type I error, such as 0.05, is *the probability that the null hypothesis will be rejected when it should have been accepted.*

A Type II error, called the beta risk, is *the probability of accepting a hypothesis when it should have been rejected.* These probabilities are the basis for operating characteristic curves used extensively in quality control work. (Computations not examined here.)

The -9.1 falls in the region of rejection and the null hypothesis is rejected. The difference of 10 percent (0.40 − 0.30) is significant at the 0.01 level. It is highly unlikely that this large a difference could be due to sampling (chance) errors. The new soup, Beefy, would probably not be successful, if marketed.

rejection

Final Self-Review Examination

First, answer all of the questions. Then check your answers against those given at the end of this chapter. Scoring: 10 problems × 10 points each = 100 possible points.

14. The engineering department has the project of increasing the tensile strength of a wire. First, 100 pieces of the wire were tested for tensile strength. The mean tensile strength was computed to be 1,000 pounds per square inch, and the standard deviation of the 100 pieces was 20 psi. As an experiment, some of the wire was treated with zonodium. A sample of 81 wires was tested. The mean tensile strength was found to be 1,200 pounds, and the standard deviation of the sample was 27 psi. Did the zonodium treatment significantly increase the mean tensile strength, or is the difference between the two means due to sampling? Use the 0.05 level of significance. The null hypothesis to be tested is _____
_____.

15. (Refer to the problem in frame #14.) Follow the usual six steps and arrive at a decision. The decision is (*a*) _____
_____.

Explain. (*b*)_____
_____

16. Two different methods of stamping out a small part are being used. Each method produces some defective parts. The problem is to determine whether one method is producing a significantly larger percent defective. A sample of 300 pieces was selected at random from the pieces produced using Method A, and it was found that 18 were defective. Out of a sample of 200 pieces produced using Method B, 10 were defective. Test the hypothesis at the 0.01 level. The decision rule is _____
_____.

17. (Refer to the problem in frame #16.) Follow the usual six steps and arrive at a decision. At the 0.01 level of significance, is it reasonable to assume that the difference between the two percent defectives is due to chance? (*a*)_____. Explain. (*b*)_____

18. Records of the scores on a scholastic aptitude test taken by prospective college freshmen revealed that the arithmetic mean score is 110 and the standard deviation is 10. These thou-

sands of scores can be considered the population. A new group just took the test, and a random sample of 400 revealed that the mean score was 106. Select one of the more commonly used levels of significance (a) _____ and indicate whether the mean of this latest group of prospective freshmen is significantly lower than the mean of past groups. The decision is (b) _____

_____.

19. (Refer to the problem in frame #18.) Was a one-tail or two-tail test used? (a) _____. Explain. (b) _____

_____

20. Past records indicate that a drug is 75 percent effective in minimizing the aftereffects of an operation. That is, 75 percent of the patients

only had slight aftereffects. The manufacturer of a new drug claims that it is as effective, or even more effective, than the one now being used. His new drug was administered to a sample of 200 patients and 120 had slight aftereffects. Accept or refute his claim at the 0.10 level of significance. Answer. _____

_____.

21. (Refer to the problem in frame #20.) The critical value used in the drug problem is _____

_____.

22. Explain what is meant by a Type I error.

_____

_____.

23. Explain what is meant by a Type II error.

_____

_____

Answers to Final Self-Review Examination

14. There is no significant difference between the mean tensile strength of the treated wire and the mean tensile strength of the untreated wire.

15. (a) Reject the null hypothesis at the 0.05 level. It is highly unlikely that the difference of 200 psi could be due to sampling.

    (b) The decision rule was to accept the null hypothesis if the critical ratio was found to be between 0 and $+1.96$ or 0 and -1.96, but reject if ± 1.96 or greater. The critical ratio z was found to be approximately -55 found by:

$$z = \frac{1,000 - 1,200}{\sqrt{\left(\frac{20}{\sqrt{100}}\right)^2 + \left(\frac{27}{\sqrt{81}}\right)^2}}$$

    so the null hypothesis was rejected at the 0.05 level.

16. Accept null hypothesis if the computed critical ratio z is between 0 and ± 2.575, reject if it falls outside those limits.

17. (a) yes

    (b) The critical ratio z was computed to be 0.5.

$$z = \frac{0.06 - 0.05}{\sqrt{\frac{0.056(0.944)}{300} + \frac{0.056(0.944)}{200}}}$$

    The 0.5 falls in the region of acceptance. The difference of 0.01 could be due to chance (sampling).

18. (a) Either 0.10, 0.05, or 0.01 are most common.

    (b) The difference of 4 points between the average of all prospective freshmen and

the average of the latest group to take the test is significant at any of the three levels selected. The computed z is -8 found by:

$$z = \frac{106 - 110}{\frac{10}{\sqrt{400}}}$$

The computed z falls in the area of rejection (outside -1.28 for the 0.10 level, or outside -1.645 for the 0.05 level, or outside -2.33 for the 0.01 level of significance).

19. (a) One-tail test used

    (b) Only interested in whether the latest group had mean test score significantly less than prior prospective freshmen.

20. Refute. The critical ratio z is about -5 found by:

$$z = \frac{0.60 - 0.75}{\sqrt{\frac{0.75(1 - 0.75)}{200}}}$$

The computed z falls in the area of rejection (beyond -1.28) so the null hypothesis is rejected. It is highly unlikely that this new drug is as effective as the one currently being used.

21. -1.28 (This is a one-tail test so look for 0.4000 in Appendix Table IV and read the approximate critical value found in the left column.)

22. A Type I error is the probability that the null hypothesis will be rejected when in fact it is true.

23. A Type II error is the probability of accepting a hypothesis when it should have been rejected.

chapter 11

An introduction to decision making under uncertanity

1 ———————————————————————

The approach to making a decision in the previous two chapters was to set up a null hypothesis, establish a decision rule, take a sample, and on the basis of the sample results make a decision. That approach might be characterized as being objective in nature and based on probability theory. In this chapter, a relatively new and different approach to decision making will be examined.

Business firms, state and local governments, the federal government, hospitals, universities, and others make numerous decisions every day. A personal decision may be to wear the brown shoes instead of the tan ones; another decision might be to buy IBM stock instead of taking a vacation. A businessman may decide to purchase modern Danish instead of early American furniture for his office.

Some decisions are made under conditions of *certainty*, but others must be made under conditions of *uncertainty*. Quotations on a new Plymouth automobile were made by two reputable dealers. One quotation was $2,795, the other $2,995 for the identical model and accessories. The decision to buy it from the dealer submitting the quotation

certainty

of $2,795 would be made under conditions of (certainty/uncertainty) _____ because all the facts were known. Another decision maker bought a home at 811 Norcross Lane instead of the one located at 19270 Valley View Drive, reasoning that the home on Norcross Lane will appreciate in value more than the one on Valley View. However, because he is not absolutely sure that this will happen, the decision was made

uncertainty

under conditions of _____.

2 ———————————————————————

Manufacturers of automobiles, drill presses, bolts, refrigerators, and so forth are dependent upon the demand of other manufacturers, wholesalers, retailers, or consumers. The demand for their output is called an *event*. Future demand for their products is uncertain. It is said that the *state of nature* (the future) is uncertain. If the manufacturer does not know whether he will sell 1,000, 2,000, or 10,000 gross next

state of nature

month, it is said that the _____ is uncertain.

3 ———————————————————————

The manufacturer (the decision maker) is not sure which state of nature (the event) will actually occur. He must produce the bolts now, however, in anticipation of next month's orders which must be filled immediately upon receipt. Under conditions of uncertainty it is said that he has a choice among several alternative *acts*. For each of these acts there are numerous possible results called *payoffs*, *consequences*, or *outcomes*.

act

If the decision maker decided to produce 27,000 gross now (called the _____),

outcome, payoff or consequence

the result (called the _____) might be a profit of $24,000, or even a loss.

4

The main parts of the decision problem under conditions of uncertainty are summarized as follows. Insert the correct word (either outcome, event, or act) opposite each group of explanatory statements.

An _____
is characterized by:

> Uncertainty regarding future demand.
> An unknown state of nature.
> A decision maker who has no control over future demand.

event

An _____
is characterized by:

> Two or more courses of action which are open to the decision maker.
> A decision maker who must evaluate various alternatives.
> A decision maker who selects a course of action based on certain criteria.

act

The _____
might be:

> Profit
> Break-even
> Loss

consequence, payoff, or outcome

5

Case of decision making under uncertainty

This case examines the decision-making process further with the objective of developing a procedure which will suggest the most profitable consequence of an act. The business fraternity on campus wants to earn money and get business experience by starting and operating a small business. One which seems to hold promise is a sports car rental agency similar to one operated by Sociable University. Plans are to rent a car to a student for $200 a week, including gas, oil, and all expenses, starting on a Friday. However, the fraternity does not have a sufficient amount of capital to buy a number of sports cars. They have been investigating an arrangement with Sports Cars, Ltd. to secure sports cars from them at $150 a week. Thus, the fraternity would earn a profit of _____ a week for each sports car rented.

$50

6

There is one problem. Sports Cars, Ltd. has other customers and must know by Wednesday of each week how many cars the fraternity wants on Friday. Thus, for the fraternity there is an element of uncertainty. If, for example, the fraternity reserves six cars on Wednesday and only four students want them on Friday, they would sustain an outright loss of _____. If they reserved four cars and four students wanted them, the total profit would be _____. Finally, if the fraternity reserved four cars and six students wanted to rent them on Friday, the total profit would be _____, but the fraternity would have lost the opportunity to make an additional _____ because the supply of cars would have been inadequate.

$100
$200

$200
$100

7 ───────────────────────────────────────

THE PAYOFF TABLE

The various combinations of demand by the students (the event) and the supply of sports cars on hand (the act) determined in the previous frame are organized into a table called a *payoff table*. In this case, to keep the computations at a minimum only events and acts of 4, 5, and 6 are considered.

Complete the payoff table. Note that each number to be inserted in the blanks is the outcome, or consequence, of a particular act and event.

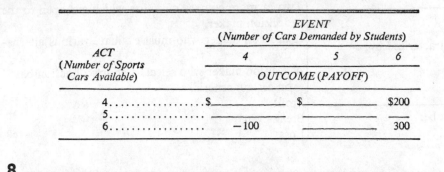

	EVENT (Number of Cars Demanded by Students)		
ACT (Number of Sports Cars Available)	4	5	6
	OUTCOME (PAYOFF)		
4..................	$_____	$_____	$200
5..................	_____	_____	_____
6..................	−100	_____	300

$200	$200	
50	250	250
	100	

8 ───────────────────────────────────────

If the previous table, called a _____ _____, was the only information available, the decision maker might consider reserving four cars from Sports Cars, Ltd. every week and be assured of earning a profit of _____. However, he might want to consider reserving five cars and hope to make a maximum of _____ instead of only $200. By reserving six cars he might earn a maximum of _____.

payoff table

$200
$250
$300

9 ───────────────────────────────────────

The payoff table in frame #7 ignores the valuable experience Sociable University has had with sports car rentals. In order to explore the problem further, the fraternity contacted SU regarding their experience. They have had the rental agency for 200 weeks and reported their demand as follows (complete the table by inserting the correct probabilities in the spaces).

Number of Sports Cars Demanded	Number of Weeks	Percent of the Total (Probability)
3..........................	0	0.00
4..........................	20	—
5..........................	140	—
6..........................	40	—
7..........................	0	—
Total..................	200	___

.10
.70
.20
.00
1.00

10 ───────────────────────────────────────

If the information in the previous table were the only data available, the decision maker (the fraternity) might decide to reserve four sports cars every week from Sports Cars,

Ltd. reasoning that four would always be demanded. However, more than four were demanded _____ percent of the weeks. If only four were reserved, the fraternity would be foregoing additional profit by not having a sufficient number available. A possible alternative would be to order six sports cars on Wednesday thus assuring that there would always be a sufficient number of cars available. Note, however, that in _____ percent of the weeks, the fraternity would have an excess number of cars. Another possible act might be to order the most frequent number of cars demanded, or _____ (number).

90

80

5

11

EXPECTED PAYOFF

Assuming that the two universities are similar, the payoff table and the experience at Sociable University are combined to arrive at the *expected payoff* of an act. This is alternatively called *expected profit* or *expected monetary value*.

Some of the calculations for the expected payoff for the act of reserving five sports cars every week from Sports Cars, Ltd. follow (complete the table).

CALCULATIONS FOR THE EXPECTED PAYOFF ON THE ACT OF
RESERVING FIVE SPORTS CARS EVERY WEEK
FROM SPORTS CARS, LTD.

Event (Demand) (Col. 1) X	Probability of Outcome Occurring* (Col. 2) $P(X)$	Payoff† (Col. 3) Y	Expected Profit (Col. 4) (Col. 2 × Col. 3) $P(X)Y$
4	0.10	$ 50	$ 5
5	.70	250	175
6	.20	——	——
		Total	——

Source: * Frame 9; † frame 7.

$250   **$50**

Total, $230

12

The total expected profit on five sports cars was found to be $230. This means that based on the experience at Sociable University, and the various payoffs from the payoff table, the fraternity could expect a profit of $230 *in the long run* if they automatically reserved five sports cars every week from Sports Cars, Ltd.

EXPECTED WEEKLY PROFIT IN THE LONG
RUN FOR THE RESERVATION OF 4, 5,
AND 6 SPORTS CARS FROM
SPORTS CARS, LTD.

Demand X	Expected Profit $\Sigma[P(X)Y]$
4	$_____
5	230
6	_____

$200

$120

The reservation of five sports cars from Sports Cars, Ltd. is only one possibility. The $230 expected profit for five cars may not result in the maximum profit in the long run. Determine the expected weekly profit for four and for six sports cars and insert the amounts in the table.

13

An analysis of the various expected profits in the foregoing table indicates that the reservation of (number) _____ sports cars will in the long run yield the

five

$230

greatest expected profit. This profit of _____ is based on the experience at Sociable University, a student rental of $200 and a reservation fee of $150 payable to Sports Cars, Ltd.

14

OPPORTUNITY LOSS

Another way of deciding on the number of sports cars to reserve from Sports Cars, Ltd. is to determine the amount of profit which might be lost because the state of nature (demand on Friday) was not known at the time the reservation was sent in on Wednesday. This potential loss is called *opportunity loss* or *regret*.

To illustrate, suppose the fraternity reserved six sports cars on Wednesday, but only four students wanted them on Friday. The fraternity would be earning no profit on the two excess cars, and the opportunity loss would be $300, found by 2 cars × $150 paid to Sports Cars, Ltd. Conversely, if the fraternity had four cars on hand and five students wanted them, not having the one additional car on hand would cost the fraternity the opportunity to make an extra $50. The $50 is the opportunity loss.

Complete the following opportunity loss table. Note that each number to be inserted is the outcome (opportunity loss) of a particular act and event.

		EVENT (Number of Cars Demanded by Students)		
ACT (Number of Sports Cars Available)		4	5	6
		OUTCOME (OR CONSEQUENCE)		
4........................		$ 0	$___	$___
5........................		___	___	___
6........................		$300	___	___

$ 50 $100
150   0   50
         150   0

15

EXPECTED OPPORTUNITY LOSS

The opportunity losses in the previous table for various levels of supply and demand again ignore the past experience of Sociable University. This past experience is used to compute the *expected opportunity loss* for one possible level of supply—five sports

COMPUTATIONS FOR THE EXPECTED OPPORTUNITY LOSS FOR THE RESERVATION OF FIVE SPORTS CARS

Demand (Col. 1) X	Probability* (Col. 2) $P(X)$	Opportunity Loss† (Col. 3) OL	Expected Opportunity Loss (Col. 4) (Col. 2 × Col. 3) $P(X)OL$
4.............0.10		$150	$15
5.............. .70		0	0
6.............. .20		50	10
			$25

Source: * Frame #9; † frame #14.

cars. The expected opportunity loss in the long run was found to be $25 a week. (See the previous computations.) This means that based on the experience at SU, the business fraternity would lose $25 a week in lost opportunities if they reserved five cars every week. Some weeks they would have the exact number on hand (5) to meet demand (5), but other weeks they would either have an excess or a shortage of rental cars. The average loss (expected opportunity loss) of $25 would result due to the inability of the fraternity to predict future demand.

The $25 may not be the lowest expected opportunity loss. Compute the expected opportunity loss for the supply of four and six sports cars respectively and insert the amounts in the following summary table.

EXPECTED OPPORTUNITY LOSS FOR 4, 5,
AND 6 SPORTS CARS

	ACT (Number of Sports Cars Available)		
	4	5	6
Expected opportunity loss.......$_____		$25	$_____

The complete table is:
$55 $25 $135

16

An analysis of the findings indicates that the lowest expected opportunity loss is ____ _____. The fraternity would experience the smallest level of lost opportunity if they reserved (number) _____ sports cars every week from Sports Cars, Ltd. To put it another way, they would have the least regret if they reserved five cars every week. The minimum opportunity loss ($25) is also called *minimax regret*.

This reinforces the decision made previously that five sports cars would give the highest level of profit ($230) in the long run. Thus, there are two ways to approach the decision, either compute the _____ profit or compute the _____ _____ loss. Both methods will suggest the same most profitable course of action.

$25

5

expected
expected opportunity

17

VALUE OF PERFECT INFORMATION

Before entering into a long-term agreement with Sports Cars, Ltd. to reserve five sports cars weekly, the fraternity might want to consider ways to determine the exact demand every week. If the fraternity knew on Wednesday that exactly four, five, or six students would want a car on Friday, it could maximize its profit by reserving the correct number. What is this advance information worth to the fraternity? That is, what is the *value of perfect information?*

The value of perfect information can be computed by subtracting the maximum profit under conditions of uncertainty from the maximum profit under conditions of certainty. The maximum profit under conditions of uncertainty was found to be $230. Now compute the expected profit under conditions of certainty. (In practice this would mean that the fraternity would know on Wednesday *exactly* how many students would demand a sports car on Friday and would reserve the cars accordingly.) If four cars were reserved and four students demanded them, the total profit would be $200, found by 4 × $50 for each car. But based on the experience at Sociable University, this demand (4) only happens 10 percent of the weeks. The average expected profit, if perfect knowledge of demand were known, would be $20, found by 0.10 × $200. These calculations are shown on the first line of the following table.

Complete the table and find the total expected profit under conditions of certainty.

CALCULATIONS OF EXPECTED PROFIT UNDER CONDITIONS OF CERTAINTY

Event (Col. 1)	Profit* Each Unit (Col. 2)	Total Profit (Col. 3) Col. 1 × Col. 2	Probability of Event† (Col. 4)	Expected Profit (Col. 5) Col. 3 × Col. 4
4........	$50	$200	0.10	$20
5........	50	_____	.70	_____
6........	50	_____	.20	_____
			Total	_____

* Based on $200 rental to students and a $150 reservation fee.
† From frame #9.

$250 $175
300   60
Total $255

18

To compute the value of perfect information:

$255

$230

$25

$_____ profit under conditions of certainty (from frame #17)
− _____ profit under conditions of uncertainty (from frame #11)
= _____ value of perfect information

Note again that the value of perfect information is also the same as minimax regret. Thus, the least amount of opportunity loss ($25 in this case) can be described by the terms "minimum expected opportunity loss," "minimax regret," and the "value of perfect information."

The fraternity should only pay up to $25 a week for perfect prediction of demand. This might be the pay for a student whose job it would be to secure advance commitments for sports cars prior to the reservation deadline on Wednesday. If the student wanted payment of more than $25 a week, the fraternity would be advised to order five cars every week because in the long run they would be assured of a profit of _____ _____ a week.

$230

Final Self-Review Examination

First, answer all of the questions. Then check your answers against those given at the end of this chapter. Scoring: 10 problems × 10 points each = 100 possible points.

19. There are three main parts to a decision problem under conditions of uncertainty. Insert the correct word opposite each group of explanatory statements. The words are: event, act, outcome.

(a) _____ Uncertainty regarding future demand. Decision maker has no control over future demand.

(b) _____ Two or more courses of action open to decision maker. Decision maker selects a course of action based on experience and other criteria.

(c) _____ Profit
Break-even
Loss

20. It is said that the state of nature is unknown. What does this mean to the decision maker?

_____

_____

Questions 21 through 28 are based on the following problem:

Two partners are considering starting an electronic repair service for manufacturers, wholesalers, and retailers. Plans include starting with a force of between six and nine electronic experts. Hourly pay would be $10 regardless of whether the repairman was on call or sitting in the office awaiting a call. The charge to the clients would be $20 an hour. A similar service in Pittsburgh, which has been operating for about 10,000 hours (approximately 5 years), revealed that:

Number of Men Demanded	Number of Hours
5	0
6	2,000
7	4,000
8	3,000
9	1,000
10	0
Total	10,000

21. Assist the partners in making a decision by determining the maximum hourly profit which would result from hiring 6, 7, 8, or 9 men. The first step is to set up a payoff table. Insert essential figures and identify the parts of the table.

22. Based on the Pittsburgh experience, set up a table of probabilities showing the event and the probability of the event.

23. Compute the expected hourly profit for 6, 7, 8, and 9 employees.

24. Based on the previous calculations, the most profitable number of men to hire is _____ _____. The hourly profit in the long run for this number is _____.

25. Another way to arrive at a decision is to determine the expected opportunity loss of certain actions. First, set up an opportunity loss table.

26. The next step is to determine the expected opportunity loss per hour for 6, 7, 8, and 9 employees.

27. The least hourly opportunity loss amounts to (a) _____ which indicates that (number) (b) _____ of employees would be the most profitable number to hire.
Now compute the value of perfect information. (c) _____ answer. It should agree with the minimum opportunity loss. Does it? (yes/no) (d) _____.

28. Briefly summarize the case and the findings.

_____

_____

_____

_____

_____

_____

_____

_____

Answers to Final Self-Review Examination

19. (a) event
    (b) act
    (c) outcome, consequence or payoff

20. It means that the future demand is unknown.

21.

ACT	EVENT			
	6	7	8	9
	OUTCOME (Payoff)			
6	$60	$60	$60	$60
7	50	70	70	70
8	40	60	80	80
9	30	50	70	90

22.

Event	Probability
6	0.20
7	.40
8	.30
9	.10

23.

Event	Expected Profit
6	$60
7	66
8	64
9	56

24. 7
    $66

25.

ACT	EVENT			
	6	7	8	9
	OUTCOME (Opportunity Loss)			
6	$ 0	$10	$20	$30
7	10	0	10	20
8	20	10	0	10
9	30	20	10	0

26.

Event	Expected Opportunity Loss
6	$13
7	7
8	9
9	17

27. (a) $7
    (b) 7 employees
    (c)

COMPUTATION OF PROFIT UNDER CERTAINTY

Event	Profit Each Unit	Total	Probability	Expected Profit
6	$10	$60	0.20	$12
7	10	70	.40	28
8	10	80	.30	24
9	10	90	.10	9
Total				$73

Then:

$73 (profit under certainty)
−66 (profit under uncertainty)
$ 7 value of perfect information

(d) Yes, it agrees with the minimum opportunity loss.

28. The partners are attempting to determine the most profitable course of action. Should they hire 6, 7, 8, or 9 employees? Based on the experience at Pittsburgh, hourly wages of $10 and an hourly fee to clients ($20), the maximum hourly expected profit was computed to be $66 for 7 employees. This was reinforced by computing the minimum expected loss ($7 an hour) for 7 employees. This was also the value of perfect information. The partners might be satisfied with less profit, such as $56 for 9 employees, and always have men available for electronics service.

Bayes' Theorem and decision making

1 ——————————————————————————

Thomas Bayes (1702–1761), an English clergyman, made a significant contribution to the area of decision making. It is called the Bayes' Theorem, or the Bayes' Rule. The rule appeared in a paper entitled "An Essay Solving a Problem in the Doctrine of Chances" published shortly after his death.

In order to illustrate the rule, suppose that a machine operator grinds a very thin disk the size of a dime plain on one side and mills a slot on the other side. Then the disks are wrapped for shipment. The operator suddenly realized that he did not machine the slot in one of the last four pieces he made, but cannot recall which one was missed. One might ask, what is the probability that one of the four pieces selected at random (say the one on the extreme right) is defective? There is (number) ————— chance out of (total number) —————————. That is, the probability P = (fraction) ————————— = 0.———. This is called a *prior* probability because it can be determined before any sampling is done or before an experiment is conducted.

one
four
$1/4 = 0.25$

2 ——————————————————————————

Suppose the same machined piece is unwrapped and tossed into the air. If it lands with a slot showing face up, the machine operator would know it (was/was not) ————— the defective one. That is, P = —————.

was not
0.00

3 ——————————————————————————

However, if the piece landed with the plain face up, what is the probability that it is the defective piece? To answer this, consider what would happen (theoretically) in the long-run if each machined piece were tossed in the air 250 times. If the piece were machined correctly, out of the 250 tosses a plain face would appear about (number) ————————— times. But out of 250 tosses, the defective piece which has two plain sides, the plain face would appear (number) ————————— times.

125
250

4 ——————————————————————————

Thus, if each piece were tossed 250 times, theoretically the following would result. Fill in the blanks. (Assume that the defective piece is on extreme right.)

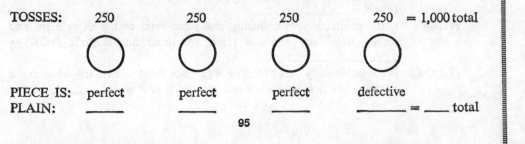

TOSSES:	250	250	250	250	= 1,000 total
PIECE IS:	perfect	perfect	perfect	defective	
PLAIN:	———	———	———	———	= ——— total

125
125
125
250
625

95

5 ───────────────────────────────

625
250
250/625 = 0.40

Thus, out of a total of 1,000 tosses, _____ plain faces would appear. And, out of the 625 plain faces, _____ would be attributed to the defective piece with two plain faces. P = (fraction) _____ = 0._____. This probability is called the *posterior* probability because it was determined *after* an experiment was conducted.

6 ───────────────────────────────

BAYES' RULE

posterior

The probability of 0.40 (frame #5), called a _____ probability, will now be determined using Bayes' Rule. In the general form, B_1, B_2 . . . . B_n are mutually exclusive events which include every possible outcome in the sample space. Suppose that A is another event in the sample space. Then $P(B|A)$ can be determined from the equation:

$$P(B|A) = \frac{P(B)P(A|B)}{\sum_i P(B)P(A|B)}$$

To put it another way, Bayes' Rule can be used to determine the probability that outcome B will occur given the additional information that outcome A has been observed.

In order to associate the letters in the general form with those being used in this problem, *Def* was arbitrarily chosen to represent a defective piece and *OK* a perfect piece. The equation then becomes:

$$P(\text{Def}|A) = \frac{P(\text{Def})P(A|\text{Def})}{P(\text{Def})P(A|\text{Def}) + P(\text{OK})P(A|\text{OK})}$$

where:

$P(\text{Def}|A)$ is the posterior probability to be determined. In this problem, it is the probability that the piece on the extreme right is defective, given an experiment or sample results A. (*The experimental result was a plain face appearing after the piece was tossed in the air.*)

$P(\text{Def})$ is the probability of choosing one of the four pieces *prior* to the experiment and finding it defective. $P(\text{Def})$ = _____.

¼ or 0.25

$P(A|\text{Def})$ is the probability that experimental or sample results A (a plain face) will appear, *assuming that a defective piece is being tossed into the air.* It is P = _____.

1

$P(\text{OK})$ is the probability of choosing one piece *prior* to the experiment and finding it perfect (one side plain, the other side slotted). $P(\text{OK})$ = _____.

¾ or 0.75

$P(A|\text{OK})$ is the probability that outcome A (a plain face) will result—*assuming a perfect piece is being tossed into the air.* It is P = _____.

½ or 0.50

7

Now, using Bayes' Rule determine the posterior probability that the machined piece on the extreme right is defective, i.e., after it was tossed in the air and it landed plain side up. (Note that the answer is the same as you found intuitively in frame #5.)

$$P(\text{Def}|A) = \underline{\hspace{4cm}} = 0.\underline{\hspace{1.5cm}}$$

$$\frac{(0.25)(1.0)}{(0.25)(1.0) + (0.75)(0.50)} = 0.40$$

8

CASE ILLUSTRATION—A PROBLEM OF SALES FORECASTING

In June the management of a department store chain requested that a forecast be made of the probable economic conditions in the area during the forthcoming Christmas selling season. The chief forecaster studied a number of economic indicators, such as the GNP, department store sales, and so on. His report to management was in the form of probabilities.

Economic Condition	Probability
Excellent	0.3
Very Good	.4
Good	.2
Poor	.1
	1.0

The forecasts are to be revised in July or August if any *additional information* becomes available. One possible source of additional information might be the dollar volume of Christmas merchandise ordered by the many departmental buyers during the summer months. The departmental buyers working independently place orders for toys, ornaments, and other Christmas gifts in quantities they believe will sell.

In order to explore total dollar volume of Christmas orders as a reliable source of additional information, the forecaster reviewed his past forecasts and the level of Christmas orders placed by the buyers during the same years. He found that when he forecasted *excellent* economic conditions for the Christmas selling season, the buyers had placed a *high* level of orders 70 percent of the years. However, 25 percent of the years their orders were of *average* size, and 5 percent of the time their orders were *low*. (The buyers worked independently of each other and were not aware of the June forecast to management.) These three probabilities can be found on the first row in the table. Fill in the remaining blanks.

Economic Forecast in June	Probability of Level of Orders During the Summer			
	High	Average	Low	Sum
Excellent	0.70	0.25	0.05	1.00
Very Good	.50	.30	.20	.
Good	.20	.30	—	1.00
Poor	.10	.40	.50	1.00

1.00
.50

9

The Bayes' Theorem can be used to revise the prior probabilities in order to determine the posterior probabilities. The $P(O_1|\text{Exc})$ of 0.70 found in the upper left corner of the following table indicates the probability is 0.70 there will be a high level of orders (O_1) given that (|) the June forecast of the economic conditions at Christmas is excellent

The probability is 0.50 a low level of orders will be placed, given a June economic forecast of poor.

(Exc). What does the $[0.50P(O_3|\text{Poor})]$ in the lower right corner of the table mean?

_____

_____

Complete the table.

Economic Forecast by Forecaster	Level of Orders from Buyers		
	High O_1	Average O_2	Low O_3
Excellent (Exc)..................0.70 $P(O_1|\text{Exc})$		0.25 _____	0.05 $P(O_3|\text{Exc})$
Very Good (VG)................ .50 $P(O_1|\text{VG})$		.30 _____	.20 $P(O_3|\text{VG})$
Good (G)..................... .20 $P(O_1|G)$		.30 _____	.50 $P(O_3|G)$
Poor (Poor)................... .10 $P(O_1|\text{Poor})$		.40 _____	.50 $P(O_3|\text{Poor})$

$P(O_2|\text{Exc})$
$P(O_2|\text{VG})$
$P(O_2|G)$
$P(O_2|\text{Poor})$

10

Recall that in June the forecaster gave management a forecast in terms of probabilities for the coming Christmas selling season, i.e., $P(\text{Exc}) = 0.30$, $P(\text{VG}) = 0.40$, $P(G) = 0.20$, and $P(\text{Poor}) = 0.10$.

Suppose the total dollar volume of orders from the buyers for Christmas merchandise has just been released. It is a *high* level of orders. Should the prior probabilities given management in June be revised upward, or downward based on this additional information?

First using Bayes' Rule, the prior probability of 0.30 (Excellent) will be revised given this recently released high level of orders.

$$P(\text{Exc}|O_1) = \frac{P(\text{Exc})P(O_1|\text{Exc})}{P(\text{Exc})P(O_1|\text{Exc}) + P(\text{VG})P(O_1|\text{VG}) + P(G)P(O_1|G) + P(\text{Poor})P(O_1|\text{Poor})}$$

$$= \frac{(0.30)(0.70)}{(0.30)(0.70) + (0.40)(0.50) + (0.20)(0.20) + (0.10)(0.10)}$$

$$= \frac{0.21}{0.46} = 0.4565$$

prior

upward
high
posterior
.4565

Thus, the probability of 0.30 sent to management in June, called the _____ _____ probability, indicating that economic conditions at Christmas would be excellent should be revised (upward/downward) _____. This revision is based on the additional information that the buyers had ordered a _____ level of Christmas merchandise. The revised probability is called the _____ probability. The prior probability of 0.30 would be revised upward to 0._____.

11

Revise the remaining prior probabilities in the following table based on the additional information (*high* level of orders) just released.

Economic Forecast	Prior Probabilities	Final Calculations for Posterior Probabilities		Posterior Probabilities
Excellent	0.30	0.21/0.46	=	0.4565
Very Good	.40	___	=	___
Good	.20	___	=	___
Poor	.10	___	=	___
Total	.	___		.

.20/.46 = 0.4348
.04/.46 = 0.0870
.01/.46 = 0.0217
1.00 .46/.46   1.0000

12

Thus, the prior probability for poor economic conditions during the Christmas selling season should be revised (downward/upward) _____ from _____ to _____ based on the _____ level of summer orders.

downward from .10
.0217   high

13

In summary, this decision problem illustrates the importance of additional information. The chief forecaster for the department store chain makes an economic forecast to management regarding the Christmas selling season in the form of probabilities, called _____ probabilities, as early as June. The importance of any new data, called _____ _____, which will allow the initial forecast to be revised is self-evident. Based on past experience, a relationship between the prior probabilities and the level orders of the buyers during the summer was discovered. This additional information allowed the prior probabilities to be revised. The revised probabilities, called _____ probabilities, will better assist management in hiring for the Christmas selling season and deciding on an advertising strategy, and they may even result in a cancellation of some orders.

prior

additional information

posterior

One weakness in the approach could be in the assigned prior probabilities. In this decision problem, they were assigned by the chief forecaster and represent his judgment. If the assistant chief forecaster had been given the job, his set of prior probabilities could have been different. The probabilities arrived at by the assistant to the assistant chief forecaster would, no doubt, be different from those of his two superiors.

There is a considerable amount of discussion in current literature regarding the role of this subjective judgment. Some argue that the statistician should not be concerned with decision problems involving subjective probabilities because by their very nature they have built-in errors. The more accepted philosophy is that Bayes' Theorem allows the decision maker to revise the initial probabilities in an orderly way when additional information becomes available.

Final Self-Review Examination

First, answer all of the questions. Then check your answers against those given at the end of this chapter. Scoring: 10 problems × 10 points each = 100 possible points.

14. There are five coins on the desk all with heads showing face up. It is known, however, that one of the coins is not a true coin and has a head on both sides. What is the probability of choosing one of the coins at random and finding it to be the imperfect coin? (a)_____ _____. This probability was determined before any experiment was conducted. Thus, it is called the (b)_____ probability.

15. One of the coins was then tossed in the air, and it landed with a head face up. Now what is the probability that it is the two-headed coin? (a)_____. This probability is called the (b)_____ probability.

    Questions 16 through 23 are based on the following decision problem.

    Before each new product is marketed nationally, a manufacturer of soaps, waxes, and other products has a panel of executives indicate its probable success. Toujour L'Amour, a newly developed soap, was rated by the executives and the composite ratings converted to probabilities.

Composite Rating	Prior Probability
Highly Successful	0.60
Moderately Successful	.30
Failure	.10
	1.00

The newly developed product is then test-marketed and the sales in the test market classified as being *above average* or *below average*.

In order that the prior probabilities of the executives and the test market results be combined to make a decision to market or not to market Toujour L'Amour, a study of the experience regarding new products within the past few years was made. It revealed that when the executive panel indicated that the product would probably be highly successful, 80 per-

cent of those products had above average sales and 20 percent had below average sales in the test market. These percents and the other results of the study are:

When Executives Indicated Product Would Be:	Sales in Test Market Were:	Percent
Highly Successful (Hi)	Above Average (AB)	80
	Below Average (BL)	20
Moderately Successful (Mod)	Above Average (AB)	60
	Below Average (BL)	40
Failure (Fail)	Above Average (AB)	10
	Below Average (BL)	90

16. In order to use the rule of Bayes, the first step is to organize the data into a table complete with abbreviations. Fill in the blanks.

Prior Opinion of Executives	Test Market Sales	
	Above Average (AB)	Below Average (BL)
Highly Successful (Hi)	0.80 P(AB|Hi)	0.20 P(BL|Hi)
Moderately Successful (Mod)	__ ___	__ ___
Failure (Fail)	__ ___	__ ___

17. Explain what the figures and designations in the upper right corner [0.20 P(BL|Hi)] mean.
_____
_____
_____
_____

18. The soap Toujour L'Amour has just been test marketed in Illinois and sales in the test market were *below average*. Now the (a)_____ probabilities can be revised using this fact called the (b)_____ to arrive at the (c)_____ probabilities.

19. Using the additional information gathered from the Illinois test market (question 18), namely, sales were *below average*, revise the initial probability of the executive panel that Toujour L'Amour will be highly successful. The answer is (a)_____. An OPTIONAL problem is to revise the prior probability that the soap will fail (again as-

suming below average sales in the Illinois test market). The answer is (b)_____.

20. Thus, the prior probability of highly success-ful, (a)_____, should be revised (up-ward/downward) (b)_____ based on the additional information that sales of the soap were below average in the test market. The posterior probability was found to be (c)_____.

21. Suppose that instead of Toujour L'Amour having below average sales in the Illinois test market they were *above average*. The posterior probability for Highly Successful would have been (a)_____.

22. Explain what the posterior probability com-puted in question 21 means. _____

_____
_____
_____.

23. What is the major purpose (or advantage) of using the rule of Bayes in decision problems? (a)_____
_____
_____
_____
_____.

What is a weakness to this approach to deci-sion making? (b)_____
_____
_____
_____
_____
_____

Answers to Final Self-Review Examination

14. (a) 1/5 = 0.20
    (b) prior

15. (a) 0.3333
    (b) posterior

16. 0.60 $P(AB|Mod)$ 0.40 $P(BL|Mod)$
    .10 $P(AB|Fail)$ .90 $P(BL|Fail)$

17. The probability is 0.20 that sales in the test market area will be below average, given an initial rating of highly successful by the panel of executives.

18. (a) prior
    (b) additional information
    (c) posterior

19. (a) .364
    (b) .272

20. (a) .60
    (b) downward
    (c) .364

21. .716

22. It means that based on above average sales in the Illinois test market, the prior probability of 0.60 for Highly Successful would be revised upward to about 0.72.

23. (a) The advantage of this approach is that the rule of Bayes allows the initial forecasts in the form of probabilities to be revised up-ward or downward as related additional information becomes available.

    (b) The weakness in this problem is that the prior probabilities represent the opinions of a panel of executives. Another panel would probably have given a different set of initial probabilities. That is, there is sub-jective judgment involved in determining the prior probabilities.

chapter 13

Chi-square

──

The chi-square test is another hypothesis-testing technique used to test (1) a set of observed frequencies with a set of hypothetical frequencies, (2) two or more sets of observed frequencies with the objective of finding out if the differences among the sets are significant. Since frequencies are the result of counting, *the chi-square test is applicable to data in discrete form.*

GOODNESS OF FIT

To illustrate the use of the chi-square test involving a set of *observed* frequencies and a set of hypothetical, or *expected*, frequencies, suppose there is some suspicion that one die being used in a dice game is loaded. The application of the chi-square test in problems of this nature is often referred to as tests of *goodness of fit*. In order to test whether the die is true, a general procedure similar to that used in testing hypotheses is followed. The usual six steps are:

Step 1. A hypothesis is stated. Again, it will be stated as a *null* hypothesis. The null hypothesis to be tested in this problem is that *the die is not loaded.* To put it another way, if the die is not loaded, and if it is thrown a large number of times, any

expected

difference between the set of observed frequencies and the set of _____ frequencies could be due to chance.

──

Step 2. A level of significance is stated. The 0.05 level was arbitrarily decided on for this test. As noted previously, other commonly used levels of significance are the 0.01 and the 0.10 levels.

Step 3. The statistic needed is identified. The statistic needed in this problem is chi-square (χ^2). It is computed by:

$$\chi^2 = \sum \frac{(f_o - f_e)^2}{f_e}$$

where:

f_o is the frequency observed.
f_e is the frequency expected.

Step 4. A critical value is determined from the table of the distribution of chi-square (Appendix Table V). The critical value of χ^2 read from the table will be the dividing point between the area of acceptance and the area of rejection. In this chi-

goodness of fit
observed

square test, called a test of _____ ____ _____, involving a set of expected frequencies and a set of _____ frequencies, the degrees of freedom are determined by $n - 1$. There are six faces on a die called *cells*, so $n = 6$. There are 5 degrees of freedom found by $6 - 1$. Referring to Appendix Table V, the critical value of chi-square for 5 d.f. and the 0.05 level of significance

11.1

is _____.

3

This critical value (11.1) is the dividing point between the area of acceptance and the area of rejection. If the computed value of χ^2 is less than 11.1, it falls within the area of acceptance, and the null hypothesis will be *accepted*. However, if the computed value of χ^2 is 11.1 or greater, it falls within the area of rejection, and the null hypothesis will be *rejected*.

Step 5. A sample is selected. In this case, the die was tossed 180 times. Even if the die is not loaded, it is not expected that the sample of 180 tosses would yield an equal number for each face of the die. However, it does seem that 3 spots and 5 spots appear more frequently and 4 and 6 spots less frequently than should be expected if the die were true.

RESULTS OF TOSSING
ONE DIE 180 TIMES

Face of Die	Number of Times Face Appeared f_o
1	25
2	26
3	48
4	16
5	50
6	15
Total	180

Theoretically, if the die were not loaded, out of 180 tosses each face (1, 2, 3, 4, 5, and 6) would appear an equal number of times, or _____ times each. This number is the expected frequency (f_e).

30

4

Step 6. Compute χ^2. Accept the null hypothesis if the computed chi-square falls within the region of acceptance but reject it if the computed χ^2 is (less than/equal to or greater than) _____ the critical value of 11.1.

equal to or
greater than

Complete the table and determine the value of chi-square.

CALCULATIONS FOR CHI- SQUARE

Face of Die	f_o	f_e	$f_o - f_e$	$(f_o - f_e)^2$	$\dfrac{(f_o - f_e)^2}{f_e}$
1	25	30	−5	25	25/30 = 0.83
2	26	30	—	—	——
3	48	30	—	—	——
4	16	30	—	—	——
5	50	30	—	—	——
6	15	30	—	—	——
Total	180	180	0		——

−4	16	16/30 = 0.53
+18	324	324/30 = 10.80
−14	196	196/30 = 6.53
+20	400	400/30 = 13.33
−15	225	225/30 = 7.50
		39.52

The computed value of chi-square is approximately _____.

39.52

5

The computed value of chi-square (39.52) is (less than/equal to or greater than) _____ the critical value of _____. Therefore, the null hypothesis is (accepted/rejected) _____ at the 0.05 level of significance. This indicates that it is highly probable that the die (is/is not) _____ loaded.

equal to or greater than
11.1
rejected
is

6 ───

To put it another way, by rejecting the null hypothesis at the _____ level, it indicates that the pattern of observed frequencies probably (would/would not) _____ _____ occur by chance.

7 ───

One of the assumptions underlying the foregoing use of chi-square is that the sample data was collected using probability methods. Specifically, in this die-tossing experiment it means that each time the die was tossed, there was an equal chance of 1, 2, 3, 4, 5, and 6 appearing face up. Also, only one face can appear each toss, i.e., the outcome is *mutually exclusive*. And, each toss is *independent* of the previous tosses.

All of the expected frequencies (f_e) in the previous illustration were equal (30). However, the expected frequencies need not be equal. Suppose that repeated polls revealed that 65 percent of the teen-age population are highly enthusiastic about a certain type of popular music, 10 percent have no opinion, and 25 percent dislike it. These percentages are assumed to be the population preferences. A sample of teenagers is to be selected at random to determine if there has been any change in preference. Before any sampling is done, however, the null hypothesis must be stated. It is

_____
_____. The 0.01 level of significance is to be used. The statistic to be computed is called _____ designated by the Greek _____. In order to locate the critical value of chi-square, the number of degrees of freedom must be determined. The d.f. are _____, found by _____.

8 ───

Referring to Appendix Table V, the critical value of chi-square is _____. This means that if the computed statistic χ^2 using sample results is less than _____ the null hypothesis will be (accepted/rejected) _____. However, if the computed value of chi-square is equal to or greater than _____ the null hypothesis will be _____.

9 ───

Recall that past records indicate that 65 percent of the teen-agers are highly enthusiastic, 10 percent have no opinion, and 25 percent dislike a certain type of popular music. Suppose the sample results were *exactly* as expected. How many teen-agers out of the 400 sampled would be highly enthusiastic about the music? _____. How many would be expected to have no opinion? _____, and how many (theoretically) would dislike the music? _____. These three numbers are called the _____ frequencies.

10 ──

These expected frequencies and the actual sample (observed) results are shown in the following table.

Teen-Age Preference	Sample Results f_o	Expected Results f_e
Highly Enthusiastic	252	260
No opinion	50	40
Dislike	98	100

Does $\Sigma f_o = \Sigma f_e$? (yes/no) _____. What is the approximate computed value of chi-square? _____.

yes (400)
about 2.79, found by
  $0.25 + 2.50 + 0.04$

11 ―――――――――――――――――――――――――――――――――

Should the null hypothesis be accepted or rejected at the 0.05 level? _____.
Reasoning? _____
_____. Does this mean that there probably has been a significant change in teen-age reaction to the music? _____.

accepted
computed
  χ^2 value of 2.79 is less than the critical value of 9.21.
no

12 ―――――――――――――――――――――――――――――――――

CONTINGENCY TABLES

Data may be classified in two ways. If the opinions of the males and females were recorded separately, the table containing these two classifications (sex and opinion) would be called a two-way classification table, or a *contingency table*. (See the left table which follows.) The table containing the music preference, by sex, has three rows (enthusiastic, no opinion, and dislike) and two columns (male, female). It is called a 3×2 contingency table.

MUSIC PREFERENCE, BY SEX

Opinion	Sex		
	Male	Female	Total
Enthusiastic	120	132	252
No opinion	24	26	50
Dislike	40	58	98
Total	184	216	400

SALES, BY MARITAL STATUS OF SALESMEN

Sales	Marital Status			
	Married	Single	Other	Total
High	213	73	18	304
Average	87	64	87	238
Low	16	99	97	212
None	1	185	158	244

The _____ table (on right) containing sales, by marital status of salesmen is a _____ $\times$ _____ table. If Jim Simpson is single and had low sales during the year, he would be one of the 99 observed frequencies shown in the table. William Hook is married and had high sales during the year. He would be one of _____ observed frequencies in the contingency table.

contingency
4×3

213

13 ―――――――――――――――――――――――――――――――――

A study of middle-management personnel is to be conducted. One of the objectives of the study is to determine what effect, if any, adjustment to marriage has on income.

Plans are to select 500 married men at random and give each one a Marital Adjustment Test (MAT). It was arbitrarily decided to subdivide the MAT scores into four classes. Incomes are to be classified into three groups.

Before any sampling is done or tests given, a null hypothesis must be formulated. It is: _____

_____. The 0.10 level of significance is to be used. As before, the statistic χ^2 is needed. To find the critical value, which is the dividing point between the area of _____ and the area of _____

_____, the degrees of freedom must first be determined. A convenient method of finding the degrees of freedom for a contingency table is: (rows − 1) (columns − 1). In this problem there are _____ rows and _____ columns. The degrees of freedom are _____.

There is *no* relationship between marital adjustment and the level of income.
  acceptance (or rejection)
  rejection (or acceptance)

  4 rows and 3
  6

14

A sample of 500 middle-management personnel were selected at random and each given the Marriage Adjustment Test. The score and the level of income of each man was recorded and then tallied in the appropriate cell. For example, John J. Jordon had a MAT of 510 and an income of $55,000. Thus, he is one of the 100 in the cell "over 500 MAT, income $50,000 and over." The observed frequencies are in the following table called a _____.

contingency table

Marital Adjustment	Under $10,000	Income $10,000–$49,999	Income $50,000 and Over	Total
Very well (500 and over)	10	40	100	150
Fairly well (300–499)	15	20	15	50
Below average (100–299)	40	50	10	100
Poor (under 100)	125	60	15	200
	190	170	140	500

Does there seem to be any relationship between marital adjustment and income? (yes/no) _____. Explain _____

_____. The counts in the various cells in the table are called the _____ frequencies.

yes
Most of the men who are very well adjusted to marriage have incomes of $50,000 and over. Conversely, most of the men who are poorly adjusted have low incomes.

observed

15

Now to determine the expected frequencies (f_e). Note in the preceding contingency table that 150 out of the 500 married men (30 percent) are very well adjusted to marriage. If there is *no relationship whatsoever* between marital adjustment and income, it can be expected that 30 percent of the 190 men who had incomes under $10,000 would be *very well* adjusted to marriage. The expected frequency (f_e) for that cell would be 57, found by 30 percent $\times$ 190. (This f_e of 57 is placed beside the f_o of 10 in the following table.) Again, if there is no relationship between marital adjustment and income, it can be expected that 30 percent of the 170 married men who had incomes in the $10,000–$49,999 range would be well adjusted. The expected frequency for that cell is _____. Further, if there is no relationship, it can be expected that 50 out of the 500, or 10 percent of the married men in any income group would be expected to be *fairly well* adjusted to marriage. For example, it would be expected that 10 percent of the 190 men (or 19 men) who had incomes under $10,000 would be fairly well adjusted to marriage.

Determine the remaining expected frequencies and insert them in the table.

Marital Adjustment	Under $10,000		Income $10,000–$49,999		Income $50,000 and over		Total
	f_o	f_e	f_o	f_e	f_o	f_e	
Very well (500 and over).............	10	(57)	40	(51)	100	( )	150
Fairly well (300–499).................	15	( )	20	( )	15	( )	50
Below average (100–299).............	40	( )	50	( )	10	( )	100
Poor (under 100).....................	125	( )	60	( )	15	( )	200
Total............................	190	( )	170	( )	140	( )	500

Due to rounding, the total of the expected frequencies for a column may not be equal to the total of the observed frequencies for that column. If this does happen, the totals should be forced to be equal by adjusting one or more of the expected frequencies in the column.

16

Recall that

$$x^2 = \sum \frac{(f_o - f_e)^2}{f_e}$$

In this problem, and starting with the upper left cell:

$$= \frac{(10 - 57)^2}{57} + \frac{(40 - 51)^2}{51} + \cdots.$$

Compute chi-square. Chi-square = _____. Arrive at a decision. The decision is to _____ the null hypothesis at the _____ level of significance. The reason is that the computed value of chi-square is _____ the critical table value of _____.

approximately 204.42

reject

0.10

more than 10.6

17

Thus, it is highly (likely/unlikely) _____ that the computed chi-square value of 204.42 is due to chance. Therefore, it is highly probable that there (is/is not) _____ a relationship between marital adjustment (as measured by the MAT) and the level of income.

unlikely

is

Certain limitations in the use of chi-square should be noted: (1) The number of cells should be 5 or more. (2) The expected number of frequencies in a cell should be 5 or more (some suggest 10). If the number of cells must be less than 5, the expected frequencies in each of the cells should be greater than 5 (some suggest 10).

The chi-square test has other uses. It can be used to determine whether or not a frequency distribution obtained from a sample follows a normal distribution. Also, it is applicable in testing whether a sampling distribution can be considered a Poisson distribution.

		42
19	17	14
38	34	28
76	68	56
190	170	140

Final Self-Review Examination

First, answer all of the questions. Then check your answers against those given at the end of this chapter. Scoring: 10 problems $\times$ 10 points each = 100 possible points.

18. Chi-square is particularly applicable when the data are in (continuous/discrete) _____ form.

19. The use of chi-square in goodness-of-fit tests implies that there is (one/more than one) (a)_____ set of observed frequencies and one set of (b)_____ frequencies.

    Questions 20 through 23 are based on the following:

    Past records revealed that 10 percent of the radio sets purchased had only the AM broadcast band, 70 percent had both AM and FM, and 20 percent FM only. A recent sample of 200 purchases revealed that 15 sets had AM only, 140 sets had AM and FM, and 45 radio sets had FM only. Has there been a significant change in the pattern of purchases?

20. The null hypothesis is _____ _____ _____.

21. The 0.10 level of significance is to be used. The critical value of chi-square is _____.

22. The computed χ^2 is _____.

23. Should the null hypothesis be accepted or rejected at the 0.10 level? (a)_____. Has there been a significant change in the pattern of purchase? (yes/no) (b)_____.

    Questions 24 through 27 are based on the following.

    Artin Corporation, a manufacturer of major appliances, wants to find out if there is any significant difference between the reasons given by former Artin owners and non-Artin owners for buying a new Artin Appliance. A random sample of 200 recent purchasers were asked to indicate the major reason why they purchased an Artin.

24. The results of the survey follow.

| | Previous Ownership | |
Major Reason for Purchase	Owned an Artin	Did not own an Artin
Style.....................	19	21
Price.....................	34	26
Reputation of manufacturer..........	57	43

Is there a significant difference between the set of reasons given by former ARTIN owners and the set of reasons given by non-ARTIN owners? The hypothesis is to be tested at the 0.05 (5 percent) level.

The previous table is a (a)_____ $\times$ _____ table, called a (b)_____ table.

25. How many degrees of freedom are there? (a)_____. The critical value is (b)_____.

26. The computed chi-square value is (a)_____. The null hypothesis is (accepted/rejected) (b)_____.

27. Explain what either accepting or rejecting the null hypothesis indicates. _____
_____
_____
_____
_____

Answers to Final Self-Review Examination

18. discrete

19. (a) one
    (b) expected

20. There has been no change in the pattern of purchases.

21. 4.61

22. about 1.88, found by: 25/20 + 0 + 25/40

23. (a) accepted
    (b) no

24. (a) 3 × 2
    (b) contingency

25. (a) 2
    (b) 5.99

26. (a) about 1.1, found by: 9/22 + 1/33 + 4/55 + 9/18 + 1/27 + 4/45
    (b) accepted

27. By accepting the null hypothesis it indicates that there is no relationship between the previous ownership pattern (owned an ARTIN or did not own one) and major reasons given for purchasing the appliance.

Statistical quality control

1

Statistical quality control is another area in which the decision rules introduced in Chapter 10 are applied. *Statistical* quality control is a relatively recent innovation. During the 17th, 18th, and 19th centuries, American industry was largely characterized by small shops making such simple hand-crafted products as candles, spoons, chairs, plows, and shoes. The individual craftsman was responsible for the "quality" of his work. The Industrial Revolution brought changes. Unskilled workers were organized into production lines with a worker performing only one operation, such as sewing on only the sole of the shoe.

The concepts of statistical quality control were developed in the 1930's by Dr. Walter Shewhart of the Bell Telephone Laboratories. His ideas were adopted by many firms mass-producing guns, bombsights, radar, and other intricate instruments during World War II. Basically, instead of inspecting every part produced (which would have been costly and very time-consuming), decisions were made based on statistical sampling techniques. For the purpose of controlling the quality, the *Shewhart Control Chart Technique* was developed for in-process manufacturing operations.

CONTROL CHARTS

Fundamental to all production is that there is no such thing as two identical parts. The difference in outside diameter from one valve stem to the next is minute (perhaps a billionth of an inch), but it is different. That is, if a more precise measuring instrument was available, a difference would be discernible.

The variation in a manufacturing process is either a *chance* cause or an *assignable* cause. Chance causes are large in number, random in nature, and cannot be entirely eliminated. For example, in making glass bottles the temperature of the mold, composition of the batch of glass, temperature of the molten glass, and so on are controlled to produce a bottle to weigh 2.0000 ounces. However, weights of 45 bottles selected at random revealed that there was variation in the weights ranging from 1.9997 ounces to 2.0003 ounces.

Weight (In Ounces)	Number of Bottles
1.9997	OO
1.9998	OOOOO
1.9999	OOOOOOOOO
2.0000	OOOOOOOOOOOOOOOO
2.0001	OOOOOOOO
2.0002	OOOOO
2.0003	O

Assuming that all of the bottles fell within the acceptable tolerances, the differences in weight were due to slight differences in the temperature of the molten glass, and other factors which were difficult, if not impossible, to identify or correct.

Assignable causes can be identified. For example, a drill is found to be dull. In another operation it was discovered that the operator was not feeding the piece of steel into the shearing machine correctly. Thus, management is mostly concerned with (chance/assignable) _____ causes. Why? _____

_____

_____

assignable. Can't do much about chance causes, but can sharpen drill, etc.

2

Therefore, the basic purpose of statistical quality control charts is to identify *when* assignable causes of variation have entered the production system. It is important, for example, to know when the drill has become dull so that remedial action can be taken immediately. Using terms common to quality control, it is important to know when production is *in control* or *out of control*. If the inside diameter of the holes falls within the specified tolerances, production is said to be *in control*. However, if the drill becomes dull and the inside diameter exceeds the specified tolerance (and production is unacceptable), the process is said to be _____ _____ _____.

out of control

One group of quality control charts has been developed for *variables* (measurable data), such as outside diameter, weights, and lengths. A second group of charts is for *attributes*. A bulb lights or it does not, there are imperfections in a panel or there are not, a part will fit or it will not. These are examples of problems requiring attribute charts.

3

Charts for variables

Bar X charts. As the name implies, bar X charts (also called *mean charts* and *X-bar charts*) are designed to portray variations in the process average. To set up a bar X chart, it is essential that the process average and standard deviation be known or estimated.

It is the usual practice in the United States to use the 99.7 percent confidence limits in quality control work. In quality control the two confidence limits are called the *upper control limits* and the *lower control limits*.

A new process is set to mass-produce a 30-ounce container, but as previously noted, variation in weight is expected because of variation in temperature of the molten glass, etc. In order to design a control chart for the process average, a sample of five containers were selected every half hour and each weighed. (See the following table.) After the 9 A.M. sample, it was decided to set up a bar X chart. The mean of the four sample means is 29.95 ounces found by 119.8/4.

WEIGHTS OF FIVE GLASS CONTAINERS SELECTED AT RANDOM EVERY HALF HOUR

Time	Weights of Sample Number					Sum	Mean	Range
	1	2	3	4	5			
7:30 A.M.	30	31	30	30	31	152	30.4	1
8:00 A.M.	29	30	28	29	30	146	29.2	2
8:30 A.M.	31	30	29	30	31	151	30.2	4
9:00 A.M.	32	28	30	30	30	150	30.0	2
							119.8	9

The centerline, or $\bar{\bar{X}}$, is 29.95 and the upper control limit and the lower control limit can be found by $\bar{\bar{X}} \pm 3\sigma_{\bar{x}}$. However, a much shorter method has been discovered using a constant A_2 and the average range $\bar{R}$. The UCL and LCL can be computed by $\bar{\bar{X}} \pm$

$A_2\bar{R}$. The average range for the four samples is 2.25, found by 9/4. The factor A_2 is found in Appendix Table II for a sample size n of 5. It is 0.577. Then:

$$\text{UCL and LCL} = \bar{\bar{X}} \pm A_2\bar{R} = 29.95 \pm 0.577(2.25) = 28.65 \text{ and } 31.25 \text{ ounces}$$

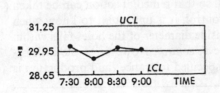

The completed bar X chart, including the means for the first four samples, is shown.

A new high-speed shearing machine is set to cut steel bars to 10.65 inches. Six pieces are selected at random every hour and the length of each checked. Construct a bar X chart based on the first three hours of operation. Show essential

LENGTHS OF SIX BARS SELECTED AT RANDOM EVERY HOUR

Time	Lengths of Sample Number					
	1	2	3	4	5	6
1 P.M.	6	7	7	8	6	8
2 P.M.	10	7	7	8	9	7
3 P.M.	8	7	7	8	7	8

figures, such as the UCL, and plot the means for the first three hours. (Note: To facilitate computations, the whole number 10 has been omitted from all the readings. Thus, the first observation at 1 P.M. should really be 10.6.)

Time	Means	Range
1 P.M.	7	2
2 P.M.	8	3
3 P.M.	7.5	1
	22.5	6

$\bar{X} = 22.5/3 = 7.5$

$\bar{R} = 6/3 = 2$

$\bar{\bar{X}} \pm A_2\bar{R} =$
   $7.5 \pm 0.483(2)$

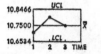

99.7
10.6534 inches and 10.8466 inches

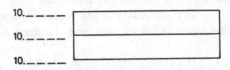

Based on this initial experience, about _____ percent of the means of samples of size six should fall between _____ and _____ inches.

4

A control chart for the mean may be misleading, if there is extreme variation in the weight. For example, note the extreme weights of the glass containers in the following table.

Time	Weights of Sample Number					Mean
	1	2	3	4	5	
7:30 A.M.	58	2	58	30	2	30
8:00 A.M.	45	1	1	45	58	30
8:30 A.M.	59	28	2	60	1	30
9:00 A.M.	3	48	4	2	93	30

Although $\bar{X} = 30$ as specified (and the mean weight of each sample was exactly 30 ounces), the extreme weights of the glass containers would no doubt result in a shut-down of the machines. What is needed then is another chart to show the variation in the ranges.

Range charts. The upper and lower control limits for a range chart are found by

$\bar{R} \pm 3\sigma_{\bar{R}}$. Instead of doing these extensive calculations, the upper control limit can be estimated by $D_4\bar{R}$ and the lower control limit by $D_3\bar{R}$.

The average range $\bar{R}$ in the glass container problem (frame #3) is 2.25, and the factor D_4 for a sample size n of 5 is 2.115 (from Appendix Table II). And, $D_3 = 0$. Then, UCL $= D_4\bar{R} = 2.115\,(2.25) = 4.75875$. The LCL $= D_3\bar{R} = 0\,(2.25) = 0$. The complete range chart, including the four ranges computed for the 7:30 A.M., 8:00 A.M., 8:30 A.M., and 9:00 A.M. samples, follows.

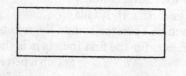

99.7% OF RANGES OF SAMPLES OF SIZE 5 SHOULD FALL IN THIS INTERVAL

Now, using the same sample data on the length of sheared steel bars from frame #3 construct a range chart in the space provided. Show essential work and plot the ranges for the 1:00 P.M., 2:00 P.M. and 3:00 P.M. samples.

$$\text{UCL} = D_4\bar{R} = 2.004(2)$$
$$= 4.008$$
$$\text{LCL} = D_3\bar{R} = 0(2) = 0$$

5

Charts for attributes

Percent defective charts. These charts are also called fraction defective charts, p charts, and $\bar{p}$ charts (pronounced p-bar charts). As the name implies, the percent defective chart portrays graphically the percent of the production which is not acceptable.

Suppose that a roll of steel exactly 200 inches long and 1 inch wide is fed into an automatic machine which cuts off a 1-inch piece and at the same time punches a hole in the center of the piece. The 200 square pieces are then moved to the assembly line. If for any reason a piece cannot be used, the worker puts it aside. The record of the first five production runs follows.

Production Number	Number of Pieces Produced	Number of Pieces Defective	Percent Defective
1	200	4	0.02
2	200	3	.015
3	200	5	.025
4	200	6	.03
5	200	2	.01
			0.10

The average percent defective ($\bar{p}$) is .02, found by:

$$\bar{p} = \frac{\Sigma \text{ of the percent defective}}{\text{Number of samples}} = \frac{0.10}{5} = 0.02 \text{ (this is the centerline on the } p \text{ chart)}$$

The upper and lower control limits are determined by:

$$\bar{p} \pm 3\sigma_{\bar{p}} = \bar{p} \pm 3 \sqrt{\frac{\bar{p}(1-\bar{p})}{n}} = 0.02 \pm 3 \sqrt{\frac{0.02(0.98)}{200}} = 0.02 \pm 3(0.0099)$$

$$= 0.02 \pm 0.0297$$

Thus, the

$$UCL = 0.0497$$
$$LCL = -0.0097, \text{ but the LCL is set at 0 (the percent defective cannot}$$
$$\text{be less than zero)}$$

The percent defective for the first five production runs is plotted on the percent defective chart.

A new high-speed shearing machine is designed to cut off 400 pieces from a long bar. The sheared pieces travel over several holes, and if a piece is too long or too short, it falls into a reject box. The machine operator counts the rejects after each 400 pieces are sheared. The number of rejects for the first four bars is shown in the following table.

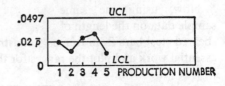

Bar Number	Number Produced	Number of Rejects
1	400	12
2	400	8
3	400	12
4	400	16

Set up a percent defective chart and plot the percent defective for the first four bars sheared.

If management was satisfied with the machine's performance, then any production over 0. _____ percent defective would be considered "out of control."

$p = 0.03$ found by 0.12/4. Then UCL and LCL =

$$0.03 \pm 3 \sqrt{\frac{(0.03)(.97)}{400}}$$

UCL = .05559; LCL = .00441

.05559 (or 5.559 percent defective)

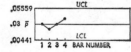

6 —————————————————————————————————

$\bar{c}$ chart. The $\bar{c}$ chart is designed to control the *number of defects per unit*. An example might be the number of defects in radio set just assembled. It might require that three solder joints be resoldered, one missing wire be inserted, and the inoperative dial light replaced. Thus, there was a total of five defects for the unit. On an automobile door three spots had to be touched up and a screw inserted in the window.

Its construction and interpretation is similar to the $\bar{p}$ chart. The UCL and LCL can be found by $\bar{c} \pm 3\sigma_{\bar{c}}$ where $\bar{c}$ is the arithmetic mean number of defects per unit. However, instead of calculating $\sigma_{\bar{c}}$ it can be approximated by $\sqrt{\bar{c}}$. Thus, the UCL and LCL = $\bar{c} \pm 3\sqrt{\bar{c}}$.

To illustrate the construction of a $\bar{c}$ chart, suppose that the number of defects per television chassis for the first 10 produced was: 4, 5, 3, 6, 0, 4, 5, 0, 7, and 6. The average number of defects per unit is: $\bar{c} =$ _____, found by _____ _____. The upper control limit is _____ and the lower control limit is _____. Now, insert these figures on the following control chart and plot the number of defects per unit for the first 10 chassis checked.

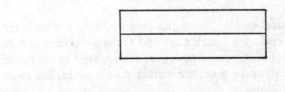

4, found by 40/10
10, found by $4 + 3\sqrt{4}$
0 $(-2$ is not realistic)

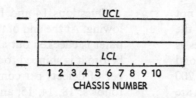

CHASSIS NUMBER

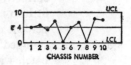

CHASSIS NUMBER

7

Based on this initial production of television chassis, the average number of defects per chassis is _____. About _____ percent of the chassis will have between _____ and _____ defects. The control chart, called a _____ chart, merely portrays the actual situation. Management must decide whether an average of four and a range of from 0 to 10 defects per unit is satisfactory. No doubt the chart would be revised after more chassis are produced.

Statistical quality control charts are utilized by most manufacturers emphasizing mass production. However, a statistical quality control department usually has other responsibilities including deciding whether to accept or reject an incoming shipment of parts. They do this based on a technique called *acceptance sampling*. Briefly, it is the technique of selecting a sample from the incoming shipment and deciding whether to accept or reject it, based on the number of defective items found in the sample.

4. About 99.7
0 and 10
$\bar{c}$

Final Self-Review Examination

First, answer all of the questions. Then check your answers against those given at the end of this chapter. Use the tables in the appendix, if necessary. Scoring: 10 problems × 10 points each = 100 possible points.

8. There are two general types of statistical quality control charts; namely, charts for _____ _____ and charts for _____ _____.

Questions 9, 10, and 11 are based on the following. A new process has just been started. The quality control inspector measures the length of four pieces every hour and records the length of each.

	Sample Piece			
	1	2	3	4
TIME	Measurements			
9 A.M.	1	4	5	2
10 A.M.	2	3	2	1
11 A.M.	4	4	4	4

9. Design a bar X chart and plot the essential data for the first three hours.

10. Design a range chart and plot the essential data for the first three hours.

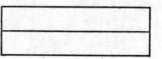

11. Now briefly interpret the two charts. _____

Questions 12 and 13 are based on the following. An automatic machine mills a slot in flat piece of steel. If the slot is not positioned correctly, or not the correct width, it will not fit into an assembly. In order to control the percent defective, the first batch of pieces is stamped automatically with a 1, the second batch with a 2, and so forth. A batch is 200 pieces. The number of defectives per batch are as shown in the following table.

Batch Number	Number in Batch	Number Defective
1	200	8
2	200	6
3	200	12
4	200	10
5	200	4

12. Construct a percent defective chart. Plot the appropriate figures, including the percent defectives for the first five batches.

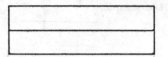

13. Briefly, interpret the chart. _____
_____
_____
_____
_____

Questions 14 and 15 are based on the following. At the end of the assembly line, a computer is checked out and the defects corrected before it is shipped to the customer. The number of defects per computer were recorded as follows: 18, 14, 15, and 17.

14. Set up a $\bar{c}$ chart based on the first four computers off the assembly line. Plot the essential data for the four computers.

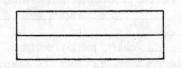

15. Briefly, interpret the chart. _____
_____
_____
_____
_____

16. Plots which fall between the upper control limit and the lower control limit indicate that the process is (a)_____ _____
_____.

17. Explain what is meant by acceptance sampling. (a)_____
_____
_____
_____

Answers to Final Self-Review Examination

8. variables and attributes

9. *Means*   *Range*
      3   4
      2   2
      4   0
    $\bar{X} = 3$ $\bar{R} = 2$
    Then: UCL, LCL $= 3 \pm A_2\bar{R}$
    $= 3 \pm 0.729(2)$

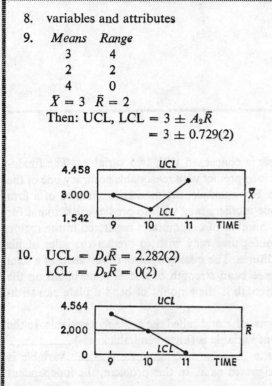

10. UCL $= D_4\bar{R} = 2.282(2)$
    LCL $= D_3\bar{R} = 0(2)$

11. About 99.7 percent of the average lengths of four pieces selected at random will vary between 1.542 and 4.458. The range of the four pieces will vary between 0 and 4.564 about 99.7 percent of the time.

12. $\bar{p} = 0.04$

    Then UCL and LCL $= p \pm 3 \sqrt{\dfrac{p(1 - p)}{n}}$
    $0.04 \pm 3 \sqrt{0.000192} = 0.04 \pm 3(0.0139)$

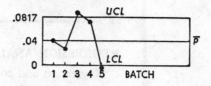

13. Based on this initial experience, 99.7 percent of the batches should be between zero percent and 8.17 percent defective with an average of 4 percent defective.

14. $\bar{c} = 16$. Then $\bar{c} \pm 3 \sqrt{\bar{c}} = 16 \pm 3 \sqrt{16} = 4, 28$

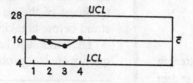

15. Based on this initial experience, 99.7 percent of the computers will have between 4 and 28 defects. The average is 16.

16. in control

17. It is a technique whereby a sample is taken from an incoming shipment and the shipment is accepted or rejected based on the number of defectives in the sample.

chapter 15

Simple regression and correlation

1 ───────────────────────────────

REGRESSION ANALYSIS

Regression and correlation analysis is concerned with two variables. The fundamental purpose of regression analysis is to predict with reasonable accuracy one of the variables based on the other variable. For example, the marketing director of a firm manufacturing replacement automobile mufflers may wish to predict the demand for the mufflers in a region based on the number of automobiles registered in the region over four years old. A perfume manufacturer may wish to predict the sales of his perfumes based on advertising expenditures. The quality control department of a steel fabricator may wish to predict the knee bend strength of a steel plate based on the thickness of the plate. (Knee bend strength is the amount of bend a plate can withstand before cracking.)

The variable to be predicted is designated Y and called the *dependent* variable. In the quality control problem, the dependent variable is (knee bend/thickness) _____ _____. Prediction of the _____ variable is based on an *independent* variable designated as X. In this problem, the independent variable is _____.

knee bend strength
dependent

thickness

2 ───────────────────────────────

The quality control engineer selected several steel plates of varying thicknesses at random and determined the knee bend strength of each. The results of the experiment are shown in the following table.

A cursory examination of the paired data, i.e., thickness and knee bend strength for each steel plate, reveals that the knee bend strength of a steel plate of, say, 4.5 inches thick (could/could not) _____ be predicted with some degree of precision. The predicted knee bend strength for the 4.5-inch plate would be *about* _____. _____ thousand pounds per square inch (psi).

could

9.5 or 9,500 psi

Thickness of Plate (In Inches) X	Knee Bend Strength (000 Pounds per Square Inch) Y
3	7
1	3
4	8
3	6
5	11

3

To further emphasize the relationship between X and Y, the paired data can be portrayed graphically in a *scatter diagram*. To plot the paired data, the dependent variable (knee bend strength in this problem) is always plotted on the Y-axis. Thus, the independent variable is always plotted on the _____. For example, the paired data for the first plot (from the previous table) is 3 inches on the X-axis and 7,000 pounds on the Y-axis. Complete the graph called a _____
_____

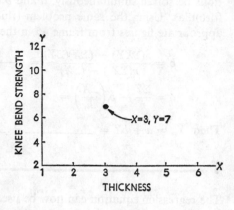

(chart labeled KNEE BEND STRENGTH on Y-axis, THICKNESS on X-axis, with point marked X=3, Y=7)

X-axis

scatter diagram

4

The scatter diagram shows: (1) As the thickness of the steel plate increases so does _____ _____ _____. (2) A straight line seems to best describe the average path of the points. (3) Any prediction of knee bend strength cannot be 100 percent accurate but can be fairly precise.

knee bend strength

5

THE LEAST SQUARES METHOD OF DETERMINING THE REGRESSION EQUATION

A linear equation, therefore, will be used as the *regression* equation. The regression equation is also called an *estimating* equation. The equation for the regression line is $\bar{Y}_p = a + bX$.

Using the least squares method, the computation of a and b in the equation, called a _____ or _____ equation, sums and other essential figures are needed. Complete the following table.

regression or estimating

Thickness X	Knee Bend Strength Y	XY	X²	Y²
3	7	21	9	49
1	3	—	—	—
4	8	—	—	—
3	6	—	—	—
5	11	—	—	—
Total —	—	—	—	—

3	1	9
32	16	64
18	9	36
55	25	121
Total 16 35	129 60	279

6

The equation for the regression line can be determined by two methods. The first method involves solving two equations simultaneously.

The second method of arriving at the regression does not require that the two equations be solved simultaneously. a and b can be found directly by using the following formulas. Using the same problem (thickness and knee bend strengths), insert the appropriate figures from frame #5 in the formulas and solve for a and b.

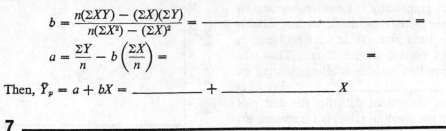

$$b = \frac{n(\Sigma XY) - (\Sigma X)(\Sigma Y)}{n(\Sigma X^2) - (\Sigma X)^2} = \underline{\hspace{3cm}} =$$

$$a = \frac{\Sigma Y}{n} - b\left(\frac{\Sigma X}{n}\right) = \underline{\hspace{2cm}} =$$

Then, $\bar{Y}_p = a + bX = \underline{\hspace{2cm}} + \underline{\hspace{2cm}} X$

$b = \frac{5(129) - (16)(35)}{5(60) - (16)^2} =$

1.93

$a = \frac{35}{5} - 1.93\left(\frac{16}{5}\right) =$

0.82

$\bar{Y}_p = 0.82 + 1.93X$

7

The regression equation can now be used to determine the points on the straight line by substituting various values for X into the equation. For example, when the thickness of a steel plate (X) is 2 inches, $\bar{Y}_p$ is 4.68, found by: $\bar{Y}_p = 0.82 + 1.93(2)$ in thousands of pounds per square inch.

This indicates that when the thickness of a steel plate is 2 inches, the knee bend strength of that plate is estimated to be 4,680 pounds. Complete the following table by determining the estimated knee bend strengths for various thicknesses.

Note that for each increase of 1 inch in thickness (X), the estimated or predicted knee bend strength ($\bar{Y}_p$) increases by _____.

Thickness (Inches) X	Knee Bend Strengths Y
1	_____
2	4,680
3	_____
4	_____
5	_____
6	_____

The complete table is:
2,750
4,680
6,610
8,540
10,470
12,400

1,930

Thus, b is defined as the average change in Y_p for each change of one (either increase or decrease) in X. $\bar{Y}_p$ is the average predicted value of the Y variable for a selected X value. The letter a in the equation is the value of Y when $\bar{X} = 0$. Another way to put it is: a is the estimated value of Y where the regression line crosses the Y-axis when X is 0. X in the regression equation is any value of X that is selected (such as 3 inches).

8

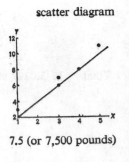

scatter diagram

7.5 (or 7,500 pounds)

7.575

Now, using the paired points ($\bar{Y}_p$ and X), the linear regression line can be plotted on the following graph called a _____ _____. One plot on the straight line is shown ($\bar{Y}_p = 4.68$, $X = 2$). Plot the remaining points. Then connect the points with a straight line.

Determine the following from the scatter diagram. If a steel plate was 3.5 inches thick, what is the approximate knee bend strength? _____ thousand pounds. Now check this approximation by using the regression equation.

$$\bar{Y}_p = 0.82 + 1.93X = \underline{\hspace{2cm}} \text{ thousand pounds.}$$

9 ━━

ERROR IN PREDICTING

Note in the preceding scatter diagram that all of the points do not fall on the regression line. If all of the plots had fallen on the straight line, and if the number of observations had been sufficiently large, there would be no error in predicting knee bend strength. That is, knee bend strength could be predicted with 100 percent accuracy. Perfect prediction in problems involving economics and business is practically non-existent. Even in this problem the thickness of the steel is not a perfect predictor of knee bend strength, probably due to slight differences in the composition of the steel.

What is needed, then, is a measure which would indicate how precise the prediction of Y is, based on X, or conversely, how inaccurate the prediction might be. This measure is called the *standard error of estimate*. One formula is:

$$s_{y \cdot x} = \sqrt{\frac{\Sigma(Y - \bar{Y}_p)^2}{n - 2}}$$

The symbol for the standard error of estimate ($s_{y \cdot x}$) represents the standard deviation of the Y's based on the X's. This measure of error, called the _____

_____, is similar in concept to the standard

deviation discussed in Chapter 5. The standard deviation measures the dispersion about an average, the standard error of estimate measures the dispersion about an average line, called the _____ line.

standard error of estimate

regression (or estimating)

10 ━━

To compute $s_{y \cdot x}$, the deviations $(Y - \bar{Y}_p)$ are needed. These are the vertical deviations from the regression line.

Complete the table.

Thickness (Inches) X	Knee Bend Strength (000) Y	Estimated Strength* (000) $\bar{Y}_p$	$Y - \bar{Y}_p$†	$(Y - \bar{Y}_p)^2$
3	7	6.61	+0.39	0.1521
1	3	2.75	———	———
4	8	8.54	———	———
3	6	6.61	———	———
5	11	10.47	———	———
Total				———

* From frame #7.
† The sum of the deviations should be 0. (Slight discrepancy due to the rounding of a and b.

Give the formula, insert the essential figures, and find the standard error of estimate.

$$s_{y \cdot x} = \quad\quad = \quad\quad \text{pounds}$$

+0.25   0.0625
— .54   .2916
— .61   .3721
+ .53   .2809
   ‾‾‾‾‾‾
      1.1592

$$s_{y \cdot x} = \sqrt{\frac{\Sigma(Y - \bar{Y}_p)^2}{n - 2}}$$

$$= \sqrt{\frac{1.1592}{5 - 2}}$$

$$= 0.62 \text{ or } 620 \text{ pounds}$$

11 ━━

CONFIDENCE LIMITS FOR PREDICTIONS

Theoretically, the standard error of estimate is a valid measure to use in setting *confidence limits* about a predicted value of $\bar{Y}_p$, if the size of the sample is large, say,

2,000 and the points on the scatter diagram are normally distributed about the regression line. If these conditions did exist in this knee bend strength problem, then the statistician would be 95 percent confident that, for a given thickness (X), the predicted knee bend strength would be somewhere between $\bar{Y}_p \pm z(s_{y \cdot x})$ or $\bar{Y}_p \pm 2s_{y \cdot x}$. Recall that the regression equation was computed to be $\bar{Y}_p = 0.82 + 1.93X$ (in thousands of pounds per square inch). The standard error of the estimate was found to be 620 psi. For a steel plate 4 inches thick, the predicted knee bend strength would be 8,540 psi, found by $\bar{Y}_p = 0.82 + 1.93(4)$. The 95 percent confidence limits would be 7,300 psi and 9,780 psi, found by 8,540 psi $\pm$ 2(620 psi).

Other z values can be found in Appendix Table IV. The procedure to find the z value was explained in Chapter 5. For the 92 percent confidence limits, it is approximately 1.75 (determined by locating 0.4600 and reading the z value in the left margin).

The 90 percent confidence limits for the predicted value of $\bar{Y}_p$ given a steel plate 5 inches thick are _____ and _____ psi. Interpret these limits_____

It should be recognized that the two assumptions (normality and a large sample) are not met in this knee bend problem. The sample size was kept small to facilitate computations. If a small sample were essential, however, a small correction factor would have to be introduced. (This correction factor will not be considered here.) Of major importance is the concept of confidence limits about the regression line.

---

12 ───

CORRELATION ANALYSIS

In the previous section, a regression line was fitted to paired data consisting of a dependent variable Y (knee bend strength) and an independent variable X (thickness). The objective was to predict knee bend strength based on the thickness of the steel plate. The error of the prediction is measured by the standard error of the estimate. If the standard error of the estimate is 0, there is no error in the prediction. All of the dots on the scatter diagram would fall on the regression line, as shown in Figure A. However, in the knee bend problem $s_{y \cdot x}$ is 620 psi indicating an error in the prediction. This is evidenced by the scatter about the regression line in Figure B.

FIGURE A   FIGURE B

$s_{y \cdot x} = 0$ $s_{y \cdot x} = 620$ psi

The 620 pounds per square inch represents the variation in knee bend strength *not* explained by the thickness of the steel. The 620 psi is difficult to interpret. Is the unexplained variation (620 psi) large or small? Further, if 620 psi is the amount not explained, what is the variation in knee bend strength explained by the thickness of the steel?

A more meaningful way of expressing the variation in Y explained and not explained by the independent variable X is in terms of percents. The proportion of the variation

---

(margin notes, left side:)

9.45 and 11.49 (in thousands of pounds) found by 10.47 $\pm$ 1.645(0.62)

The statistician is 90 percent confident that if a steel plate 5 inches thick were selected at random, the knee bend strength would be between 9,450 pounds and 11,490 pounds.

in Y *explained* by X is called the *coefficient of determination* (r^2). The variation in the dependent variable Y not explained by the independent variable X is called the *coefficient of nondetermination*, found by $1 - r^2$. It is designated by either $1 - r^2$, or k^2.

The value of either coefficient may vary from 0 to 1. A coefficient of determination of 0 indicates that none of the variation in Y is explained by the X variable. A coefficient of determination of 1 indicates that _____
_____. An r^2 of 0.91 would suggest that a large part of the variation in the Y variable is determined by the X variable. (The computation of the coefficient of determination will be shown shortly.)

all, or 100 percent, of the variation in Y is explained by X.

13

The square root of the coefficient of determination is called the *correlation coefficient r*. A convenient formula for computing the correlation coefficient follows. Note that the numerator in the formula is the same as used in determining b in the regression equation. All the essential numbers were computed in frame #5. Find the correlation coefficient, coefficient of determination, and the coefficient of nondetermination.

$$r = \frac{n(\Sigma XY) - (\Sigma X)(\Sigma Y)}{\sqrt{[n(\Sigma X^2) - (\Sigma X)^2][n(\Sigma Y^2) - (\Sigma Y)^2]}}$$

$$= \qquad = 0.\_\_\_\_$$

The coefficient of determination (r^2) is 0._____ and the coefficient of nondetermination 0._____.

.98, found by
$$\frac{5(129) - (16)(35)}{\sqrt{[5(60) - (16)^2][5(279) - (35)^2]}}$$

.96
.04

14

Now interpret the coefficient of determination _____
_____
_____ and the coefficient of nondetermination (which is often called the coefficient of alienation). _____

96 percent of the variation in knee bend strength is explained by the thickness of the steel.
4 percent of the variation in knee bend strength is not attributable to the thickness.

The coefficient of correlation (r) is 0.98. It is defined as the degree of relationship, or the degree of correlation, between knee bend strength and the thickness of the steel plates. The meaning of the coefficient of correlation is not as explicit as that of the coefficient of determination. In a problem such as the one involving knee bend strength and thickness, Y increases as X increases. Thus, the correlation coefficient can have a value from 0 to $+1$ with zero indicating no relationship and $+1$ indicating perfect relationship between the two variables. In this problem, 0.98 indicates _____
_____.

0.98 indicates a high degree of relationship between knee bend strength and thickness.

15

In the knee bend problem, there is a *positive* relationship, i.e., as X (thickness) increases Y (strength) (increases/decreases) _____. However, the correlation coefficient can be *negative*. For example, note in Figure A that as the price (X) of the commodity increased, the sales _____.

increases

decreased

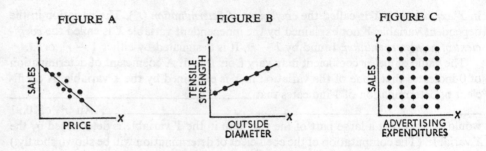

FIGURE A — SALES vs PRICE

FIGURE B — TENSILE STRENGTH vs OUTSIDE DIAMETER

FIGURE C — SALES vs ADVERTISING EXPENDITURES

−1	Thus, the correlation coefficient can have a value between +1 and _____
+1	inclusive. Refer to Figure B. What is the approximate coefficient of correlation? _____
Diameter is a perfect predictor of strength.	_____. What does the coefficient indicate? _____
About 0. There is practically no relationship.	_____. Refer to Figure C. What is the approximate coefficient of correlation? _____. What does this indicate? _____

Final Self-Review Examination

First, answer all of the questions. Then check your answers against those given at the end of this chapter. Scoring: 10 problems × 10 points each = 100 possible points.

All of the questions are based on the following problem.

A personnel director has the responsibility of selecting new salesmen. In order to make the best selection possible from a group of job applicants, he designed a placement test which he called the DOT test. His objective is to predict the level of sales of an individual based on his DOT test score. However, in order to determine whether there is any relationship between his DOT test and sales he asked several veteran salesmen to take the test. Their test scores and their average weekly sales are shown in the following table. (In practice, many more paired observations would be needed.)

Salesmen	DOT Test Score	Weekly Sales ($000)
Sam Jones	3	$5
Bob Patten	4	7
Jim Farmer	2	4

16. Does it appear that the personnel director will be able to predict the sales of an applicant based on his DOT test score? (yes/no) (a)_____. Which variable is the dependent variable? (b)_____

17. In order to portray this relationship graphically, plot the paired data in a graph called a (a)_____ _____. The DOT test scores, which are the (dependent/independent) (b)_____ variable, must be plotted on the (c)_____ axis. (Label the axes.)

18. Determine the equation for the straight line which will pass through the paired points. The line is called a (a)_____ or _____ line. The equation is (b) $\bar{Y}_p =$ _____ = _____ (Carry calculations to the nearest hundredth, such as 1.68.)

19. Plot the line on the scatter diagram in frame #17. Give the calculations for one point on the straight line. (a)_____

Mr. James Coffman is an applicant for a position as salesman. He scored 6 on the DOT test. Based on the regression equation (frame #18), what is his predicted average weekly sales? (b)$_____.

20. Assume that the standard error of estimate was computed to be $.1, i.e., $100. What is the 98 percent confidence limit for Mr. James Coffman's predicted weekly sales (from frame #19)? (a)$_____ and $_____

Interpret the confidence limits (b)_____
_____

21. The coefficient of determination is 0. (b) Interpret _____
_____

22. The coefficient of nondetermination is (a)_____.
Interpret (b)_____
_____

23. The coefficient of correlation is (a)_____.
Interpret (b)_____
_____

24. The proportion of the explained variation is called the (a)_____.
The degree of relationship between X and Y is measured by the (b)_____.

25. Briefly summarize the problem, the measures of regression and correlation used to solve the problem, and draw some observations based on the measures computed. _____
_____
_____
_____
_____

Answers to Final Self-Review Examination

16. (a) yes
    (b) sales

17. (a) scatter diagram
    (b) independent
    (c) X-axis

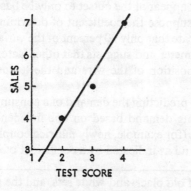

18. (a) regression or estimating
    (b) $\bar{Y}_p = a + bX = 0.83 + 1.50X$

19. (a) When $X = 2$, $\bar{Y}_p = 3.83$ (found by $\bar{Y}_p$
    $= 0.83 + 1.5(2)$
    When $X = 3$, $\bar{Y}_p = 5.33$, and when X
    $= 4$, $\bar{Y}_p = 6.83$
    (b) 9.83 or $9,830$

20. (a) $9,597 and $10,063, found by $9,830 \pm 2.33 ($100)
    (b) The personnel manager would be 98 percent confident that if an applicant scored 6 on the DOT test he would sell between $9,597 and $10,063 a week. To put it an-

other way, 98 out of 100 weeks an applicant with a test score of 6 should sell between $9,597 and $10,063.

21. (a) 0.96
    (b) 96 percent of the variation in sales are explained by the test score.

22. (a) 0.04
    (b) 4 percent of the variation in weekly sales of an individual are not accounted for by the DOT test.

23. (a) 0.98
    (b) There is an extremely high degree of relationship between the test score and sales.

24. (a) the coefficient of determination
    (b) the coefficient of correlation

25. The personnel manager wanted to predict with reasonable accuracy the weekly sales of a salesman based on a test score. If there were a high correlation between his DOT test score and sales, the test would be very useful in hiring new salesmen. A small group of veteran salesmen took the test, and the test score of each paired with his sales. The relationship between the two variables is excellent ($r = 0.98$). About 96 percent of the variation in sales is explained by the test score. The regression equation $\bar{Y}_p = 0.83 + 1.50X$ can be used to predict the sales of a salesman. The error in the prediction is measured by the standard error of estimate ($100).

Multiple regression and correlation

1

The simple linear regression and correlation analysis in the previous chapter dealt with *two* variables. The basic objectives were to determine the degree of association between the two variables and to arrive at an equation which might be used to predict one variable (Y) designated as the (dependent/independent) _____ variable, based on an independent variable (X). Recall that one measure of the degree of association is called the coefficient of _____. It may have a numerical value between 0 and $\pm$ _____. The linear predicting equation (called a regression equation) is in the form of $\overline{Y}_p =$ _____ _____.

2

Although useful, simple regression and correlation considers only the relationship between *one* independent variable and the dependent variable and ignores the possible effect of any other independent variable which might be related. To illustrate the point, the tensile strength of steel wire might appear at the outset to only be based on the outside diameter of the wire. However, suppose the coefficient of determination (r^2) was computed to be 0.90. This would indicate that only 90 percent of the variation in tensile strength is attributable to outside diameter and suggests that other factors contributed to tensile strength, such as the composition of the wire and the temperature of the furnace.

The same logic might be applied to predicting the demand of a consumer good, such as new color television sets. Predicting demand based on one independent variable, such as the number of new consumers (for example, newly married couples), might not fully explain all the variation in demand as indicated by a coefficient of determination of 0.74. What does the 0.74 indicate? _____

_____. Replacement of old black-and-white sets, and the purchases of a second or third set for the home are other factors which might also be contributing to demand.

3

Because of the large number of calculations needed, hand calculations or desk calculators are seldom used now to solve real-world multiple regression and correlation problems. Instead, a number of computer programs are available. These programs vary in the degree of complexity. The accompanying print-out is from IBM program #60.148, called the *Single and Multiple Linear Regression Analysis*. Briefly, the problem involves three independent variables and a dependent variable. The multiple regression equation and a number of measures needed to describe the degree of association between the three independent variables and the dependent variable are found on the print-out. On the pages following the print-out, various measures will be examined.

```
ZZJOB 5
ZZFORX54
ZZJOB 5
ZZFORX54
17136 CORES USED                    39999 NEXT COMMON
SINGLE AND MULTIPLE LINEAR REGRESSION ANALYSIS
  CAMILLE KASPRZAK STAT 217

NUMBER OF INDEPENDENT VARIABLES =   3
NUMBER OF DATA POINTS          =  10
 17702.   1535.   8717.   2127.
 21139.    674.  13248.   2490.
 18969.    570.  11011.   3205.
 15890.    630.   9737.   2528.
 26247.    984.  15488.   4233.
 20680.    888.  10219.   3998.
 14081.    874.   8592.   2794.
 20080.    708.  12802.   2696.
 28420.   1740.  16002.   4879.
 10134.    536.   6029.    847.
SUM OF VARIABLES

SUM Y=  .19334200E+06
SUM X 1=  .91390000E+04     SUM X 2=  .11184500E+06
SUM X 3=  .29797000E+05     SUM X

MEAN OF VARIABLES

MEAN Y=  .19334200E+05
MEAN X 1=  .91390000E+03    MEAN X 2=  .11184500E+05
MEAN X 3=  .29797000E+04    MEAN X

PARTIAL REGRESSION COEFFICIENTS
      J           B(J)
      0        .70536140E+03
      1        .22608850E+01
      2        .11729390E+01
      3        .11557810E+01

REGRESSION EQUATION

    Y=  .70536140E+03      +  .22608850E+01 X( 1)+  .11729390E+01 X( 2)+
        .11557810E+01 X( 3)+

COEFFICIENT OF DETERMINATION=  .97137591E+00
MULTIPLE CORRELATION COEFFICIENT  =        .98558404E+00
STANDARD ERROR OF THE ESTIMATE    =        .11198373E+04
SIGNIFICANCE OF REGRESSION (F)    =        .67871196E+02
STANDARD ERROR OF PARTIAL REGRESSION COEFFICIENTS
      0        .14327771E+04
      1        .10501002E+01
      2        .19228958E+00
      3        .56322346E+00
PARTIAL CORRELATION COEFFICIENTS X(L) TO X(J)
  L       J          R(L,J)
  1       1        .10000000E+01
  1       2        .38018140E+00
  1       3        .49969637E+00
  2       2        .10000000E+01
  2       3        .79194722E+00
  3       3        .10000000E+01
```

Suppose that the sales analyst of a large firm which manufactures and distributes automotive parts wants to make an annual sales forecast for each of the 10 sales territories. There are several factors which he thinks are related to the annual level of sales in a territory: (1) The number of retail outlets in the territory carrying their parts. (2) The average number of new automobiles sold per month in the territory. (3) The total personal income in the territory. The number of new automobiles sold is published every month by the state registrar of motor vehicles, and the federal government releases the personal income figures by state for the first quarter of the year in April.

Thus, if there is found to be a relationship between the three variables and sales, the analyst could gather the figures for each territory in April and predict the sales for the entire year. In order to determine if there is a relationship, the analyst collected the sales, called the (dependent/independent) _____ variable, the number of outlets, new automobile registrations, and the total personal income for each territory for last year. The number 3 in the following print-out indicates that _____

dependent

there are 3 independent variables

10 sales territories

and the number 10 indicates _____
_____.

```
NUMBER OF INDEPENDENT VARIABLES =   3
NUMBER OF DATA POINTS           =  10
```

4 _____

Territory	Annual Sales Y	Retail Outlets X_1	New Cars X_2	Personal Income X_3
1	17702.	1535.	8717.	2127.
2	21139.	674.	13248.	2490.
3	18969.	570.	11011.	3205.
4	15890.	630.	9737.	2528.
5	26247.	984.	15488.	4233.
6	20680.	888.	10219.	3998.
7	14081.	874.	8592.	2794.
8	20080.	708.	12802.	2696.
9	28420.	1740.	16002.	4879.
10	10134.	536.	6029.	847.

The analyst arbitrarily decided to record the sales (Y) to the nearest million dollars. For example, the sales in territory #1 for last year were actually $17,702,000. (See the accompanying printout.) There were 1,535 retail outlets (X_1), and a monthly average of 8,717 new cars registered (X_2) in the territory. Five zeros have been omitted from the X_3 dependent variable so the first-quarter personal income was $212,700,000 for territory #1. Briefly, from left to right, interpret the four figures for territory #2. _____
_____
_____.

annual sales (Y) $21,139,000

674 retail outlets (X_1)
13,248 average monthly new car registrations (X_2)

$249,000,000 first-quarter personal income (X_3)

5 _____

MULTIPLE REGRESSION

The multiple regression equation

The simple linear regression equation $\bar{Y}_p = a + bX$ portrays the *average* regression between two variables. The multiple regression equation merely extends the simple regression equation to include the many independent variables being used to predict the one dependent variable. Complete the general form of the multiple regression equation applicable to this problem.

$$\bar{Y}_p = a + b_1X_1 + b_2X_2 + \underline{\hspace{3cm}}$$

b_3X_3

6 _____

In the multiple regression equation a is a constant. The various b values are also constants (weights) applied to their respective independent variable. They are called b coefficients, *beta coefficients*, or *net regression coefficients*. In the computer print-out, they are called *partial regression coefficients*. The first number (.70536140) is a, but note that the decimal must be moved three places to the right. Then $a = 705.36140$. What is the b_1 coefficient? _____.

```
PARTIAL REGRESSION COEFFICIENTS
            J         B(J)
            0     .70536140E+03
            1     .22608850E+01
            2     .11729390E+01
            3     .11557810E+01
```

2.2608850

7

The beta coefficient of 2.2608850 indicates that if the number of retail outlets in the territory increased by 1, annual sales would increase by $2,260. (The other variables are assumed to remain constant.) Interpret the meaning of the b_2 coefficient. _____

_____. The complete equation, called the _____ _____ _____ _____ for this problem is (insert actual numbers in the equation):

$\bar{Y}_p = $ _____

For each increase of one new automobile registration, annual sales will increase $1,172. (This assumes that the other variables remain constant.)

multiple regression equation

$$\bar{Y}_p = 705.36140 + 2.2608850X_1 + 1.1729390X_2 + 1.1557810X_3$$

8

To illustrate its use, suppose that in some future year the analyst wanted to predict the annual sales in a certain territory. There were 900 retail outlets in the territory, the average monthly new car registrations were 11,000, and the federal government released the estimated first quarter personal income to be $300 million. So $X_1 = 900$, $X_2 = 11,000$, and $X_3 = 3,000$ (because five zeros have been omitted). The predicted annual sales for the territory would be $19,089,360, found by (some digits omitted to facilitate computations):

$$\bar{Y}_p = \underset{\substack{\text{constant}\\a}}{705.36} + \underset{b_1 \text{ (firms)}}{2.26(900)} + \underset{\substack{b_2 \text{ (new}\\ \text{cars)}}}{1.17(11,000)} + \underset{\substack{b_3 \text{ (personal}\\ \text{income)}}}{1.16(3000)}$$

Also, suppose that the analyst wanted to use the multiple regression equation in another territory to estimate annual sales. There were 800 retail outlets, a monthly average of 10,000 new cars registered, and the first-quarter personal income estimate was $250 million. Predicted annual sales for the territory is _____.

$17,113,360, found by $705.36 + 1,808 + 11,700 + 2,900 (in thousands of dollars)

9

Multiple standard error of the estimate

The multiple regression equation gives an *average* predicted value of Y for selected values of $X_1, X_2, \ldots X_n$. This means in this case that unless the relationship is perfect, the actual sales at the end of the year will not always be *exactly* the same as the sales prediction made in April. Thus, in practical business problems, there is usually some discrepancy between the predicted value and the actual value. This error in prediction can be measured by the *multiple standard error of estimate*.

In the previous chapter (simple correlation), the standard error of estimate was based on the squared deviations from the regression line. It measured the dispersion or scatter about the linear regression line. In multiple regression, it measures the dispersion or scatter about the multiple regression plane. That is, the standard error of estimate measures the deviations of the actual Y values from the predicted values ($\bar{Y}_p$). The formula is quite similar to the one used in simple regression.

In this case, it is the standard deviation of Y (sales), based on X_1 (retail outlets), X_2 (new cars), and X_3 (personal income).

The computer calculated the standard error to be $1,119,837.

STANDARD ERROR OF THE ESTIMATE   =   .11198373E+04

The multiple standard error of the estimate is used in the same manner as the standard error of the estimate was used in the two-variable simple regression case. Assuming there are a large number of territories and the values of Y (sales) are somewhat normally distributed around the regression plane, then:

$$\bar{Y}_p \pm 1(S_{y.123}) \text{ encompasses about 68 percent of the actual } Y \text{ values (sales)}$$
$$\text{around the regression plane.}$$

Using the predicted sales of $19,089,360 from frame #8 [given 900 firms (X_1), 11,000 new cars (X_2), and $300 million personal income (X_3)] the two limits are about $18.0 million and $20.2 million, found by:

$$\$19,089,360 \pm 1 (\$1,119,837) = \$17,969,523 \text{ and } \$20,209,197 \text{ (or rounded,}$$
$$\$18.0 \text{ million}$$
$$\text{and } \$20.2$$
$$\text{million)}$$

To put it another way, if there were a large number of territories with the same three combinations (900, 11,000, and $300 million), it could be expected that in about _____ percent of the territories the actual annual sales would be between approximately $18.0 million and _____ million, with the average sales being about _____ million. And, 95 percent of the annual sales would be between $\bar{Y}_p \pm 2S_{y.123}$, and so forth.

68
$20.2
$19.1

10

MULTIPLE CORRELATION

THE COEFFICIENT OF DETERMINATION

The multiple standard error of estimate which measures the *unexplained* variation in sales is rather difficult to interpret. Is a $S_{y.123}$ of $1,119,837 relatively large or small? A standard error of estimate of zero can be easily interpreted by saying that all (100 percent) of the variation in Y (sales) is explained by the number of retail outlets (X_1), new cars (X_2), and personal income (X_3). A more useful way of expressing the variation in Y explained and not explained by X_1, X_2, and X_3 is in terms of percents. The percent of the variation in the dependent variable (sales) explained by the three independent variables is called the *coefficient of determination*. It is designated as R^2, and it can assume a value between 0 and $+1$ inclusive.

COEFFICIENT OF DETERMINATION= .97137591E+00

Interpret the coefficient of determination in this problem. _____

_____

97.1 percent of the variation in the annual sales of a territory is explained by the number of retail outlets (X_1), the number of new cars (X_2), and the personal income (X_3) in the sales territory.

coefficient of nondetermination
about 0.029, found by
$1 - 0.971$

11

THE COEFFICIENT OF NONDETERMINATION

The *coefficient of nondetermination*, found by $1 - R^2$ indicates the percent of the variation in Y not explained by the three independent variables. $1 - R^2$, called the _____ _____ is _____

for this problem. Interpret it _____
_____.

about 2.9 percent of the variation in annual sales is not explained by the three independent variables.

12

MULTIPLE CORRELATION COEFFICIENT

The *multiple correlation coefficient* in this problem is:

```
MULTIPLE CORRELATION COEFFICIENT =        .98558404E+00
```

It is the square root of the coefficient of determination, and it is designated as R. Multiple R is interpreted the same as the simple correlation coefficient, i.e., it indicates the degree of relationship or association between Y (the dependent variable) and the independent variables. However, unlike the simple correlation coefficient, the multiple correlation coefficient cannot be negative. Its value is between 0 and $+1$. Interpret the multiple R in this problem. _____
_____.

The .985 coefficient is very close to $+1$ and therefore indicates near-perfect relationship between sales and the three independent variables.

Some of the most useful measures in multiple regression and correlation analysis have been discussed in the preceding frames. A complete analysis of the relationship between a dependent variable and several independent variables would require a study of all the measures on the print-out, plus others found in more detailed computer programs. For example, not discussed was the F statistic of 67.87 which indicates that the relationship is significant, i.e., it is highly unlikely that this relationship could be due to chance.

It is of interest that the IBM 1620 required less than 30 seconds to compute all these measures. Using a desk calculator, it is doubtful whether they could be determined in 30 hours.

Final Self-Review Examination

First, answer all of the questions. Then check your answers against those given at the end of this chapter. Scoring: 10 problems × 10 points each = 100 possible points.

13. Discuss the advantages of multiple regression and correlation analysis compared with simple regression and correlation. _____
_____
_____
_____

14. The general form of the multiple regression equation is: _____
_____

15. Suppose that a multiple regression equation is:
$\bar{Y}_p = 16.18 + 0.06X_1 + 21.01X_2 + 2.14X_3 +$

$3.4X_4 - .87X_5$. The b_4 of 3.4 indicates _____
_____
_____.

16. The error in predicting using the multiple regression equation is measured by the _____
_____
_____.

17. Interpret a coefficient of determination of 0.81.
_____
_____
_____

18. If the coefficient of determination is 0.81, what is the correlation coefficient? (a)_____
Interpret (b)_____
_____
_____

19. If the coefficient of determination is 0.81, what is the coefficient of nondetermination? (a)_____ _____ Interpret (b)_____

_____

_____

20. In multiple regression and correlation analysis the value of the coefficient of determination, the coefficient of nondetermination and the correlation coefficient may be between 0 and

+1. (true/false) (a)_____. If false, explain (b)_____

_____

21. The variable to be predicted in a multiple regression problem is called the _____ _____ variable.

22. In general, what is the F test? _____

_____

_____

Answers to Final Self-Review Examination

13. The use of simple correlation in real business problems usually indicates that say only 70 percent of the variation in Y is based on the one independent variable (X). This indicates that there are other variables which must be affecting the dependent variable Y. Multiple regression and correlation analysis includes the possible effect of many variables on the dependent variable.

14. $\bar{Y}_p = a + b_1X_1 + b_2X_2 + \cdots b_nX_n$

15. For each increase of 1 in the variable X_4, $\bar{Y}_p$ will increase by 3.4. (assuming that the other variables remain constant).

16. standard error of the estimate

17. 81 percent of the variation in $\bar{Y}_p$ is attributable to the independent variables (X_1, X_2, and so on)

18. (a) 0.90, found by $\sqrt{0.81}$; (b) There is a high degree of association (+1 is perfect correlation).

19. (a) 0.19; (b) 19 percent of the variation in $\bar{Y}_p$ is not attributable to the independent variables.

20. true

21. dependent

22. It is a test made to determine if the relationship (correlation) is significant, or whether it could be due to chance.

Time series analysis

1

A time series is a set of data taken periodically, usually yearly, quarterly, monthly, or weekly. Examples of a time series are the annual sales of the IBM Company since 1952, and the monthly production of automobiles since 1949.

One purpose of analyzing data over a period of time is to make long-term or short-term forecasts. Long-term forecasts of sales, production, or imports might be for 5, 10, 15, or 20 years. These forecasts are made to assist management in developing a strategy and alternative strategies. For example, The United States Forest Service revealed that in 1960 ten billion board feet of lumber were used, but by 1980, the demand will be 15 billion, and by 2000, the demand will be 21 billion board feet.[1] (The strategy of Georgia-Pacific to meet this demand is to plant five trees for every one cut down.)

Short-term forecasts, usually of under one year, are common. Examples are predictions of the level of Christmas sales, third-quarter employment, and "Government officials are prepared for—and expect—the rate of unemployment to reach 4 percent by the end of the year."[2]

---

[1] *Forbes*, July 15, 1968, p. 15
[2] *Business Week*, July 20, 1968, p. 18

2

COMPONENTS OF A TIME SERIES

Using the classical approach to time series analysis, data over a period of time has four components: namely, (1) long-term or secular trend, (2) cyclical variation, (3) seasonal variation, and (4) irregular or random variation.

The following production series contains monthly data since 1920. The dashed line characterizes the average

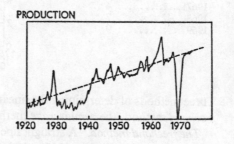

PRODUCTION

1920 1930 1940 1950 1960 1970

upward movement, or the long-term secular trend, of production since 1920. It is called the *secular trend* line. Note that there is considerable cyclical variation above and below the _____ _____ line.

secular trend

3

SECULAR TREND

There are many types of growth curves which can describe the long-term movement of a business and economic series. The dashed line drawn through the sales series in Figure A typifies the growth in sales from 1948. Describe the growth. _____

Sales had an initial period of slow growth followed by a period of rapid growth. In recent years sales have leveled off.

The straight line drawn through the production series in Figure B best describes the trend in production since 1950.

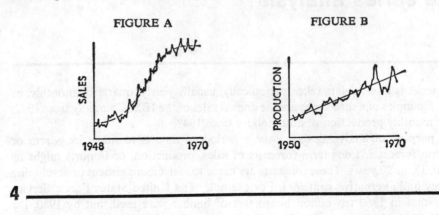

FIGURE A   FIGURE B

4

STRAIGHT-LINE (LINEAR) TRENDS

Arithmetic straight-line trend

If the long-term trend pattern tends to follow a straight line when plotted on arithmetic graph paper, it indicates that the trend line is increasing (or decreasing) at a constant absolute amount. The imports of an item is an illustration. (The number of time periods have been kept at a minimum to facilitate computations.)

Year	Imports ($ Billions)
1965	$3
1966	5
1967	4
1968	7
1969	9

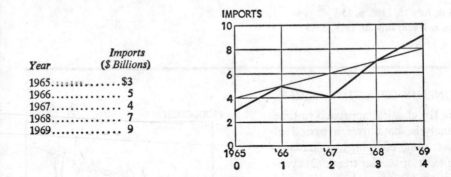

Three methods of determining the linear-trend equation will be examined: namely, the *freehand* method, the *semiaverage* method, and the method of *least squares*.

The freehand method. A straight line has been drawn through the data shown in the preceding graph. The year 1965 is designated as the origin, or zero year. The year 1966 is coded 1; 1967 is coded 2; . . . and 1969 is coded 4. Note that the line intercepts the Y-axis in the zero year (1965) at \$_____ billion. This is a in the linear equation $\bar{Y}_p = a + bX$. Also note on the straight line representing imports that the imports increased from about \$4 billion in 1965 to about \$_____ billion in 1969. Imports increased on the average \$4 billion (\$8 − \$4) in the four year period, or \$_____ billion a year. This is b. Thus, the straight-line equation using the _____ method is:

$$\bar{Y}_p = \underline{\hspace{1cm}} + \underline{\hspace{1cm}} X$$

where: imports are in billions, the origin (or zero year) is 1965, and X increases by 1 unit for each year (i.e., 0, 1, 2, etc.)

4

8

1

freehand

$\bar{Y}_p = 4 + 1X$

5

Plot the following production data. Connect the points by straight lines. Then, using the freehand method draw a straight line through the plots.

Years	Production (000 Units)
1964..............	5
1965............	9
1966............	7
1967..........	8
1968..............	10
1969............	9

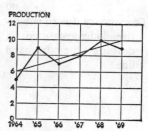

PRODUCTION

The _____ method was used to estimate the straight line trend.

freehand

The linear trend equation is (approximately) $\bar{Y}_p =$ _____

$\bar{Y}_p = 6 + 0.8X$

Based on the linear trend equation, estimated production for 1971 is ____.____ 000 units.

11.6 thousand

6

The semiaverage method. Two averages are determined in order to find the trend line. Using the following data on imports, the average of the first half is $4 billion computed by $3 + $5 + $4/3. The average of the other half is $6.66 billion, computed by $4 + $7 + $9/3. (There is an *odd* number of years and it was arbitrarily decided to include the $4 billion for 1967 in both averages.)

Year	Imports ($ Billions)
1965........	$3 ⎤
1966........	5 ⎥ $\frac{$12}{3}$ = $4 average
1967........	4 ⎦
1968........	7 ⎤ $\frac{$20}{3}$ = $6.66 average
1969........	9 ⎦

Note that imports rose from the average of $4 billion in 1966 to $6.66 billion in 1968, or a $2.66 billion increase in two years. Thus, the average annual increase is $1.33 billion, found by $2.66/2. This ($1.33 billion) is *b*. The trend line value of $5.33 billion for 1967 was found by adding $1.33 billion to the 1966 trend line value of $4 billion. Then, the average increase in imports ($1.33 billion) was added to $5.33 billion to arrive at the 1968 trend value. What is the trend equation? _____ X

$\bar{Y}_p = 2.67 + 1.33X$

7

The linear-trend equations determined using the freehand method ($\bar{Y}_p = 4 + 1X$) from frame #4 and the semiaverage method ($\bar{Y}_p = 2.67 + 1.33X$) are not identical. The discrepancy is caused by the subjective judgment involved in drawing the freehand line. Four different individuals might arrive at four different equations for the data on imports. However, the freehand method can be used when a quick approximation of the trend equation is needed.

If there are an *even* number of years, the averages for the two halves can be computed directly. Compute the linear-trend equation using the semiaverage method for the production data from frame #5 (repeated as follows):

Year	Production (000 Units)
1964......................	5
1965.....................	9
1966.....................	7
1967.....................	8
1968.....................	10
1969.....................	9

semiaverage

$\bar{Y}_p = 6.34 + 0.66X$

$\bar{Y}_p = 6 + 0.8X$

no

Discrepancy due to subjective judgment used in drawing the freehand line.

The equation using the _____ _____ method is:

$\bar{Y}_p =$ _____

The equation using the freehand method from frame #5 is _____

_____ Are the two equations identical? (yes/no) _____

If not, why not? _____

_____

8 _____

The least squares method. The least squares method of finding the straight line gives the "best fitting" line. (It can be demonstrated that the sum of the squared deviations from the least squares trend line is less than the sum of the squared deviations from either the line determined using the freehand method or the semiaverage method.)

Using the least squares method, and the import data given previously, the trend equation will be computed. To arrive at the equation, the sums, squares, and other figures needed are shown in the following table: n is the number of years. In this problem there are five years.

Year	Imports ($ Billions) Y	X	XY	X²	Y²
1965	$ 3	0	0	0	9
1966	5	1	5	1	25
1967	4	2	8	4	16
1968	7	3	21	9	49
1969	9	4	36	16	81
	$28	10	70	30	180

Two equations are solved simultaneously. They are:

$$\text{I: } \Sigma Y = na + b\Sigma X$$
$$\text{II: } \Sigma XY = a\Sigma X + b\Sigma X^2$$

$$28 = 5a + 10b$$
$$70 = 10a + 30b$$

Equation I can be multiplied by 10, and Equation II by 5 to eliminate a:

$$(10 \times) 280 = 50a + 100b$$
$$(5 \times) 350 = 50a + 150b$$

Subtracting Equation II from Equation I:

$$\text{I: } 280 = 50a + 100b$$
$$\text{II: } 350 = 50a + 150b$$
$$-70 = -50b$$
$$b = 1.4$$

The b value of 1.4 can be substituted in Equation I or Equation II to solve for a.

$$\text{Equation I: } 28 = 5a + 10b$$
$$28 = 5a + 10(1.4)$$
$$14 = 5a$$
$$a = 2.8$$

The equation is $\bar{Y}_p = 2.8 + 1.4X$ where imports are in billions of dollars and 1965 is the origin or zero year.

Using the same production figures (frame #5), plot the data. Then determine the linear trend equation using the least squares method. The equation is _____ where production is in _____

_____ and the origin is _____

_____. The _____ method was used. Determine the coordinates for the straight line and plot the line. Two coordinates are:

$$X = 0, \bar{Y}_p = \text{_____, and}$$
$$X = 4, \bar{Y}_p = \text{_____}$$

Using the equation, the projected production for 1975 is _____ units.

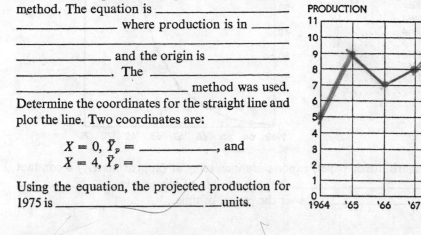

The two equations are:
$$48 = 6a + 15b$$
$$132 = 15a + 55b$$

$$\bar{Y}_p = 6.25 + 0.7X$$

thousands of units
1964
least squares

6.25
9.05

13.95 (13,950 units)

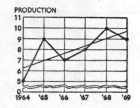

9

Semilogarithmic straight-line trend

A semilogarithmic straight-line trend is appropriate when the series of sales, production, and so forth is considered to be increasing or decreasing at a somewhat constant *rate*. Thus, an arithmetic straight-line equation should be used if overall the data is increasing (or decreasing) at a somewhat constant (amount/rate) _____ and a semilogarithmic straight-line equation should be used if the data is changing at a somewhat constant _____ .

amount
rate

10

The differences in the two series are shown in Figure A and Figure B.

FIGURE A

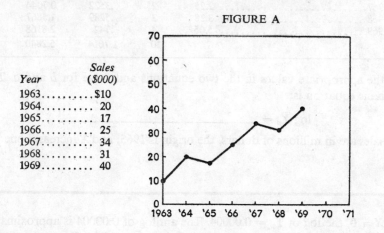

Year	Sales ($000)
1963	$10
1964	20
1965	17
1966	25
1967	34
1968	31
1969	40

Plotted on arithmetic paper, sales on the average are increasing at (approximately) a constant _____ , but the rate of increase is _____ over the period of time.

amount   decreasing

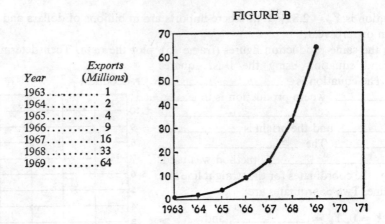

FIGURE B

Year	Exports (Millions)
1963	1
1964	2
1965	4
1966	9
1967	16
1968	33
1969	64

Plotted on arithmetic paper, exports are increasing at (approximately) a constant _____ but the amount of increase is _____ _____ over the period of time.

rate
increasing

11

The semilogarithmic trend equation can be found using the least squares method. The two equations to be solved simultaneously are:

$$\text{I:} \quad \Sigma \log Y = na + b\Sigma X$$
$$\text{II:} \quad \Sigma X \log Y = a\Sigma X + b\Sigma X^2$$

Sales in the following table appear to be increasing at a somewhat constant rate (about 50 percent). The sums and other figures needed to find the trend line equation follow.

Year	Sales ($ Millions)	X	log Y	X log Y	X²
1965	$1.00	0	0.0000	0.0000	0
1966	1.50	1	.1761	0.1761	1
1967	2.25	2	.3522	0.7044	4
1968	3.38	3	.5289	1.5867	9
1969	5.06	4	.742	2.8168	16
		10	1.7614	5.2840	30

Insert the appropriate values in the two equations and solve for b and a. The semilogarithmic equation is:

$$\log \bar{Y}_p = \underline{\hspace{4cm}}$$

where sales are in millions of dollars, the origin is 1965, and X increases one unit each year.

$\log \bar{Y}_p = .00004 + .1761X$

12

When $X = 0$, the log of $\bar{Y}_p = 0.00004$. The antilog of 0.00004 is approximately 1.00. Thus, one of the coordinates on the line is $X = 0$, $\bar{Y}_p = 1.00$. Determine the $\bar{Y}_p$ value when $X = 4$ _____. The forecast of sales for the year 1973 is _____.

approximately 5.07
approximately 25.7

13

Now plot the three points on the semilogarithmic graph paper.

The straight-line trend is (arithmetic/semilogarithmic) _____. Being semilogarithmic, b represents a *percent* change in Y for each increase of one in X. The logarithm of b is 0.1761 and the antilog of that number is _____. This indicates that sales have been increasing about 50 percent on the average from 1965 to 1969. The forecast for 1973 of $25.7 million is based on an average annual increase of _____ percent.

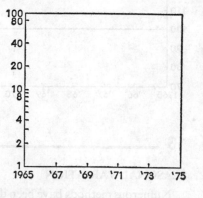

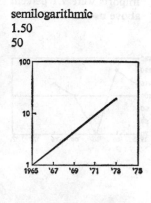

14

Prices of an electronic part have been increasing as follows:

Determine the semilogarithmic straight-line trend equation using the least squares method: $\log \bar{Y}_p =$ _____ _____. Prices have been increasing about _____ percent on the average year.

Years	Prices
1966	$1.92
1967	2.40
1968	2.89
1969	3.57

The equations to be solved
$$1.6771 = 4a + 6b$$
$$2.9601 = 6a + 14b$$

$$\log \bar{Y}_p = 0.2859 + 0.0889X$$

about 23 percent

15

CYCLICAL VARIATION

Most businesses have periods of prosperity, recession, depression, and recovery. These movements are called *business cycles* if the duration of the cycle is more than a year. The annual data from frame #8 is used to illustrate how the cycle is isolated from the time series. The annual dollar volume of imports contains trend and cycle, designated by TC. If the original data are divided by trend (T), a cyclical relative (index) results. That is $[TC/T](100) = C$. Or, $[Y/\bar{Y}_p](100) = C$.

The straight-line equation from frame #8 is $\bar{Y}_p = 2.8 + 1.4X$ where imports are in billions and 1965 is the origin. Complete the table.

Year	Imports Y	$\bar{Y}_p$	$\dfrac{Y}{\bar{Y}_p}$	Cyclical Index C
1965	$3	$2.8	$\left[\left(\dfrac{3}{2.8}\right)\right]$	$(100) = 107.1$
1966	5	4.2	$\left[\left(\dfrac{5}{4.2}\right)\right]$	$(100) = 119.0$
1967	4	___	___	( ) = ___
1968	7	___	___	( ) = ___
1969	9	___	___	( ) = ___

The original data and the trend line are portrayed as follows.

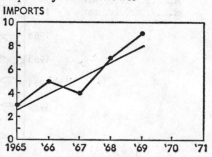

$\bar{Y}_p$	$Y_p/\bar{Y}_p$	C
$5.6	(4/5.6)	(100) = 71.4
7.0	(7/7.0)	(100) = 100.0
8.4	(9/8.4)	(100) = 107.1

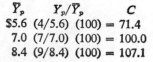

In 1967, imports were 28.6 percent below normal (i.e., 28.6 percent below the long-term trend). Imports were 7.1 percent above normal in 1969.

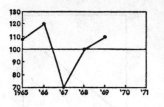

Plot the cyclical indexes.

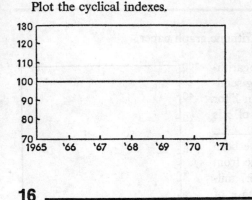

Imports were 7.1 percent above normal in 1965 and 19.0 percent above normal in 1966 (a period of relative prosperity). Interpret the 1967 and 1969 indexes.

_____

_____

_____

_____

16

SEASONAL VARIATION

Numerous methods have been developed to measure the typical seasonal fluctuation in a time series. The methods vary from a rather simple approach to sophisticated methods employing electronic computers. Four such methods are: (1) a method using averages, (2) a ratio-to-trend method, (3) a commonly used ratio-to-moving-average method, and (4) an exponential smoothing method.

The purpose of employing one of these methods is to isolate seasonal (S), i.e., exclude the other three components of a time series; namely, _____, _____, and _____. The usual procedure is to start with a monthly series such as sales, production, or other data which may, or may not, have a repetitive seasonal pattern. The sales of a department store (Exhibit 1) are used for illustration. In order to determine whether the series does have a definable seasonal pattern, a *tier* chart may be drawn (Exhibit 2). Note that the department store usually has periods of high sales in the spring and at Christmas and relatively low sales _____ and _____

_____. Using one of the methods mentioned (or others) a *typical seasonal* pattern is determined (Exhibit 3). These typical seasonals are in the form of indexes. The average of the 12 _____ _____ indexes is 100. The typical seasonal indexes have been plotted (Exhibit 4).

(in any order) trend, cycle, irregular

the first few months of the year, and during the summer

typical seasonal

EXHIBIT 1

Sales ($000), 1963

Jan.	$401
Feb.	398
Mar.	403
Apr.	416
etc.	etc.

EXHIBIT 2

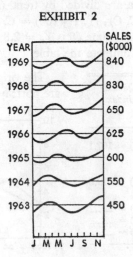

YEAR	SALES ($000)
1969	840
1968	830
1967	650
1966	625
1965	600
1964	550
1963	450

J M M J S N

EXHIBIT 3

Typical Seasonal Indexes

Jan.	86.2
Feb.	81.3
Mar.	99.6
Apr.	101.3
May	98.7
June	97.1
July	99.8
Aug.	101.2
Sept.	103.6
Oct.	105.1
Nov.	110.9
Dec.	115.2

EXHIBIT 4

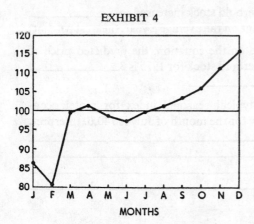

MONTHS

The typical seasonal index of 86.2 for January indicates that typically the sales of this department store are 13.8 percent below the average for the year. The typical seasonal index of 115.2 for December indicates that _____ _____ _____.

Typical December sales are 15.2 percent above the average for the year

The typical seasonal pattern, which is a composite of past experience, can be used by the management of the department store to make comparisons with the typical seasonal pattern of all department stores. It can also be used as a bench mark against which current sales can be compared. For example, this year management tried several new sales innovations during the months of January and February. The seasonal index for those two months dropped to 95.6 and 93.8 respectively. Sales were still below the average for the year (100), but how did sales for those two months this year compare with sales during a typical January and February? (From Exhibit 3.) _____.

The sales promotion was apparently a success. Sales for January and February of this year were above the typical sales for January and February determined from past experience.

Final Self-Review Examination

First, answer all of the questions. Then check your answers against those given at the end of this chapter. Scoring: 10 problems × 10 points each = 100 possible points.

17. The four components of a time series are _____, _____, _____ _____, and _____.

18. Plot the following sales data and estimate the straight-line trend equation using the freehand method. The trend equation is: (a)_____ _____

Year	Sales ($000)
1964	$ 2
1965	6
1966	4
1967	6
1968	10
1969	8

What is one weakness to the freehand approach? (b)_____ _____

_____
_____

19. Now, using the semiaverage method, determine the linear-trend line for the sales data shown in frame #18. (Carry calculations to the nearest hundredth, such as 2.68.) The equation is _____

20. Referring again to the sales data (frame #18), determine the arithmetic straight-line trend equation using the least squares method. The equation is _____ _____.

21. Based on the straight-line trend equation (frame #20) the predicted sales for 1975 are $_____.

22. Based on the same equation (frame #20), the cyclical index for 1966 is (a)_____ _____. Interpret (b)_____ _____ _____

23. The per-share price of Amberbold Limited increased as shown.

Year	Price
1966	$ 6.81
1967	8.74
1968	11.20
1969	14.50

A cursory examination of the data revealed that the price of Amberbold stock has been increasing at a somewhat constant rate (about 30 percent a year on the average). Thus, a semilogarithmic straight-line trend equation should be used. The equation is _____.

24. Based on the semilog equation, the price of

Amberbold stock increased _____ percent on the average a year. (nearest percent)

25. Based on the equation, the predicted price of Amberbold stock for 1975 is $_____.

_____.

26. The typical seasonal index for motel occupancy for the month of July is 140.6. Interpret.

_____

_____

_____

_____

Answers to Final Self-Review Examination

17. (In any order) trend, cycle, seasonal, irregular.

18. (a) $\bar{Y}_p = 3 + 1.4X$
    (b) Subjective judgment is involved drawing the freehand line.

19. $\bar{Y}_p = 2.67 + 1.33X$

20. $\bar{Y}_p = 2.85 + 1.26X$

21. $16.71 (or $16,710)

22. (a) 74.5, found by (4/5.37)(100)
    (b) Sales in 1966 were 25.5 percent below the trend line.

23. The two equations are
    I : $3.9852 = 4a + 6b$
    II: $6.5241 = 6a + 14b$
    $\log \bar{Y}_p = 0.83241 + 0.10926X$

24. Over 28 percent

25. $65.40, found by $\log \bar{Y}_p = 0.83241 + 0.10926(9)$

26. Typically, motel occupancy in July is 40.6 percent above the average for the year.

Indexes

1

A typical television, radio, or newspaper release might be "Consumer prices rose again this month, according to the U.S. Department of Commerce. The Consumer Price Index was up one tenth to 128.4, meaning that prices this month were 28.4 above those in 1957, 1958, and 1959." In addition to the well-known Consumer Price Index, there are hundreds of indexes published on a daily, weekly, monthly, quarterly, and annual basis by the federal government, universities, financial institutions, and others.

To illustrate the construction of an index, assume that the annual production of bituminous coal was 4 billion tons in 1962 and 5 billion tons in 1969. The index of production for 1969, based on 1962, was 125, computed by dividing 5 billion tons by 4 billion tons and then multiplying by 100; that is, $[5/4](100) = 125$.

If the price of Grade D plywood was $200 a thousand board feet in 1965 and $180 in 1969, the price index for plywood for 1969 based on 1965 (1965 = 100) is: _____.

90

2

Note that:

1. An index is actually a percent. The percent sign is seldom given, however.
2. Each index has a *base* period. The base period of the Consumer Price Index is 1957–59.
3. The base number of practically all indexes equals 100. There is no specific reason, however, why 10, 1,000, or any other number cannot be used as a base.
4. Most indexes are carried either to the nearest tenth, such as the Consumer Price Index of 128.4 from frame #1, or to the nearest whole number such as the bituminous coal index of 125.
5. If the base is 100, the percent change from the base period to the current month or year can be easily determined. For example, the Consumer Price Index of 128.4 indicates that prices increased _____._____ percent from the base period to the current month. The price index of 90.0 for plywood indicates that the price of plywood (increased/decreased) _____ by _____ percent from 1965 to 1969.

28.4

decreased
10

3

One might ask, Why are such indexes as the Consumer Price Index and indexes of industrial production, department store sales, and so on, compiled and published? Indexes facilitate a comparison and analysis of unlike series, such as production, employment, prices, and sales, by establishing a base period and converting subsequent numbers into percents (indexes). Converting data to indexes also makes it easier to compare the trend in a series composed of exceptionally large numbers. For example, if the total sales of a product were $295,932,456.94 in 1962, and increased to $296,044,-529.00 in 1969, the increase would appear significantly large. The 1969 sales expressed as an index based on 1962 sales however, is 100.04. This indicates that sales increased only _____.

Furthermore, an index is also a convenient way of expressing a change in the total of a heterogeneous group of items. The Index of Industrial Production, for example, includes many different items, such as steel production, television production, and automobile production, expressed in tons, barrels, yards, each, and many other different units.

Economists and others watch the Consumer Price Index and other index series for signs of excessive inflation, recession, and so forth. Some labor-management contracts have escalator clauses in them automatically providing a specified increase in wages should the Consumer Price Index rise a given number of points. Businessmen compare changes in their production or prices with other firms or the industry using indexes.

4 ───

CONSTRUCTION OF INDEXES

Unweighted index numbers

Unweighted indexes are also called *simple* indexes, or *relatives*. The base for the following illustration was arbitrarily chosen as 1966. The index for 1969 is 150, found by $60/40 times 100. Complete the table.

Year	Bale Price of Jute	Index (1966 = 100)	
1965	$36	_____ = ____
1966	40	[$40/$40](100) = 100.0
1967	46	_____ = ____
1968	53	
1969	60	[$60/$40](100) = 150.0

5 ───

The relative (index) for 1969 of 150.0 using 1966 = 100 indicates that _____ _____. If the average of 1966 and 1967 were selected as the base (written 1966–67 = 100), the price relative (index) for 1969 would be _____._____

6 ───

A slightly more complex problem would be to determine an index of food prices. Assume for this illustration that the typical family eats only three food items: bread, milk, and pomegranates. An unweighted index of food prices for 1969 in the following example would be computed by dividing the total of the prices for 1969 (p_n) by the 1965 (p_o) total. That is:

$$P = \frac{\Sigma p_n}{\Sigma p_o}(100) = \text{————}(100) = \text{————}.\text{————}$$

Margin notes (left column):

4/100 of 1 percent

[$36/$40](100) = 90.0

[$46/$40](100) = 115.0
[$53/$40](100) = 132.5

the price of jute increased 50% from 1966 to 1969
139.5, found by [$60/$43] (100)

$P = \frac{164¢}{130¢}(100) = 126.2$

Item	1965 Price p_o	1969 Price p_n
Bread (loaf)............................30¢		28¢
Milk (quart).........................40		36
Pomegranates (box)...........................60		100
Total.................................... —		—

$$\Sigma p_o = 130¢ \quad \Sigma p_n = 164¢$$

7

The method used in the preceding example is not appropriate. The unweighted price index of 126.2 seems illogical because the two major food items (bread and milk) decreased and only pomegranates, which are eaten infrequently, increased. It seems logical, therefore, that the prices of bread and milk should be given more *weight* than the price of pomegranates.

Weighted indexes

The same data from frame #6 is used to illustrate the construction of a *weighted* price index. The consumption of each food in the base period of 1965 is given in the second column and is designated q_o. To determine the total amount spent for food in the base period, the quantity of each food item consumed is multiplied by the corresponding price. Find the total amount spent for food in the base period by completing the middle column.

In order to measure the effect of price, an assumption is made that the amount of food consumed by a typical person did not change between the base period (1965) and 1969. The 1969 prices (p_n) are multiplied by the corresponding quantities consumed in 1965. Complete the right column in the following table designated as $p_n q_o$.

Item	1965 Price p_o	1965 Amount Consumed q_o	$p_o q_o$	1969 Price p_n	$p_n q_o$
Bread (loaf).....................30¢		2,000	$600.00	28¢	$560.00
Milk (quart).....................40		500	——	36	——
Pomegranates (box)..............60		2	——	100	——
Total.....................			$__.__		$__.__

$200.00	$180.00
1.20	2.00
$801.20	$742.00

8

Determine the weighted index of price for 1969 using 1965 as the base.

$$P = \frac{\Sigma p_n q_o}{\Sigma p_o q_o}(100) = \underline{\hspace{2cm}} (\underline{\hspace{1.5cm}}) = \underline{\hspace{2cm}}.$$

$$\frac{\$742.00}{\$801.20}(100) = 92.6$$

9

The unweighted price index of 126.2 computed in frame #6 indicated an increase of 26.2 percent in the price of food from 1965 to 1969. The price index found using the

The composite price of food declined 7.4 percent from 1965 to 1969.

The two major food items (bread and milk) declined in price, but only one minor item (pomegranates) increased in price. Thus, it is logical that the index is under 100.

weighted method (92.6) gives a more logical answer. Interpret the index of 92.6

_____

Why is weighted index of 92.6 a more logical answer? _____

_____

_____

10

Using the weighted method to compute a price index, the quantity in the base period is held constant. This method was developed by Etienne Laspeyres in the 1700's.

The Laspeyres method of weighting is also used to compute a quantity index. The prices in the base year (1964) are held constant in the following illustration in order to determine the index of industrial production. Complete the table and find the weighted index of industrial production.

Item	1964 Price p_0	1964 Quantity Produced q_0	p_0q_0	1969 Quantity Produced q_n	p_0q_n
Automobile (each).............	$2,000	10	$_____	9	$_____
Oil (barrel)......................	4	800	_____	1,000	_____
Transformers (each).............	100	40	_____	300	_____
Color film (roll)..................	2	1,000	_____	5,000	_____
Total....................			$_____		$_____

(left margin)

p_0q_0	p_0q_n
$20,000	$18,000
3,200	4,000
4,000	30,000
2,000	10,000
$29,200	$62,000

$$\frac{\$62,000}{\$29,200}(100) = 212.3$$

$$Q = \frac{\Sigma p_0q_n}{\Sigma p_0q_0}(100) = \underline{\hspace{3cm}} = \underline{\hspace{2cm}}$$

11

In addition to price indexes and quantity indexes, there are *value* indexes and *special-purpose* indexes. As the name implies, a value index measures the change in the total value of a group of products, commodities, and so on. A value index, such as the well-known Index of Department Store Sales, needs both the base-year prices and base quantities and the present-year prices and present-year quantities for its construction. Complete the following table.

COMPUTATIONS FOR A VALUE INDEX

Item	1959 Price p_0	1959 Quantity Sold q_0	p_0q_0	1968 Price p_n	1968 Quantity Sold q_n	p_nq_n
TV sets (each).........	$400	50	$_____	$500	30	$_____
Cologne (set)..........	5	300	_____	4	200	_____
Shoes (pair)..........	10	1,000	_____	20	1,500	_____
Girdles (each)..........	4	2,000	_____	4	3,000	_____
Total..........			$_____			$_____

(left margin)

p_0q_0	p_nq_n
$20,000	$15,000
1,500	800
10,000	30,000
8,000	12,000
$39,500	$57,800

The Index of Department Store Sales is found by dividing the total dollar volume of sales in 1968 by the total dollar volume of sales in the base period (1959). Design a formula, insert essential figures in the formula and find the index.

$V =$ _____ = _____ . _____

$$V = \frac{\Sigma p_n q_n}{\Sigma p_o q_o}(100) =$$

$$\frac{\$57,800}{\$39,500}(100) = 146.3$$

12

Special-purpose indexes are usually a combination of a number of price, quantity, and value indexes. The Forbes Index and the Business Week Index are two examples of _____-_____ Index. Various indicators and indexes selected by the statistician are arbitrarily weighted by him to find the composite weighted index. For example, note in the following table that in the judgment of the statistician, the Industrial Production Index should be weighted 50 percent. The Employment Index was arbitrarily weighted 30 percent and Money Turnover 20 percent. To determine the composite (weighted) index of business activity for 1968, the production index of 110.0 was weighted by 0.50, employment of 120.0 by 0.30, and money turnover by _____. The index of 109.0 computed by 55 + 36 + 18 for 1968 indicates that general business activity was up 9.0 percent over the 1964 level. Compute the index of business activity for 1969. _____ . _____ (answer). The index of business activity for 1969 indicates that_____

_____

_____

special purpose

20

103.0
general business activity increased three percent from 1964 to 1969.

Year	Industrial Production Index Weight...0.50	Employment Index 0.30	Money Turnover 0.20
1964	100.0	100.0	100.0
1968	110.0	120.0	90.0
1969	108.0	116.0	71.0

13

CRITERIA FOR THE CONSTRUCTION OF AN INDEX

One criterion for the selection of a base period for an economic and business index is that conditions be somewhat normal. Why wasn't 1933 given consideration as a base year?_____

a depression year

Changes in the basic consumption pattern dictate a revision of an index and a change in the base period from time to time. For example, outboard motors and phonograph records are now included in the CPI.

Another important consideration in the construction of an index is the selection of the items to be included and the weight allocated to each item. The Consumer Price Index includes about 400 consumer items, and the Wholesale Price Index about 2,000. In the Consumer Price Index, beer has a relative weight of 1.06 percent, indicating that _____ . _____ percent of a typical consumers income is spent on beer.

1.06

14 ─────────────────────────────────────

SHIFTING THE BASE

If two or more series being compared are not on the same base, it is difficult to make any meaningful comparison between the series. Suppose that the increase in the prices received by farmers and the increase in all wholesale prices from 1964 to 1969 are to be compared. Note in the following table that the Index of Prices Received by Farmers is on a 1910–14 base, but the Wholesale Price Index is on a 1957–59 base. Complete the table by shifting both series to a 1964 base (1964 = 100).

Year	Index of Prices Received by Farmers 1910–14 = 100	Index of Prices Received by Farmers 1964 = 100	Wholesale Price Index 1957–59 = 100	Wholesale Price Index 1964 = 100
1964	236	$\frac{236}{236}(100) = 100$	98.0	100.0
1965	248	$\frac{248}{236}(100) = 105.0$	102.1	104.2
1969*	292	─( ) = ──	125.0	──

Source: *Survey of Current Business.*
* Estimated.

Farm Index = $\frac{292}{236}(100)$ = 123.7
W.P.I. = 127.6, found by $\frac{125.0}{98.0}(100)$

15 ─────────────────────────────────────

Now that the two series are on a common base, make a comparison of the change in prices from 1964 to 1969. _____

_____

_____

Contrary to the initial examination of the figures, wholesale prices increased at a more rapid rate (27.6 percent) than did farm prices (23.7 percent) between 1964 and 1969.

16 ─────────────────────────────────────

SPECIAL USES OF THE CONSUMER PRICE INDEX

Real income

The Consumer Price Index measures the change in prices of goods and services bought by city wage earners' and clerical workers' families from one time period (1957–59) to another time period. The CPI has a number of other applications. One use is to determine the "*real*" income of individuals. Two other popular terms are *deflated income* and *income expressed in constant dollars*.

To illustrate the concept of real income, assume that Mr. Typical Wage Earner had an income of $6,000 in 1965, and the base of the Consumer Price Index was shifted to 1965, i.e., 1965 = 100. His income this year is estimated to be $12,000 and the CPI 200. It appears, that since his income doubled, that his standard of living is higher than in 1965. Note, however, that although his *money income* doubled from $6,000 to $12,000, the prices Mr. Typical Wage Earner pays for food, gasoline, clothing, and other items also doubled. Thus, his standard of living remained the same from 1965 to the present time. So his buying power (real income) is still $6,000. The computations for real income are as shown in the following table:

Year	Money Income	Consumer Price Index 1965 = 100	Real Income
1965	$ 6,000	100	$\frac{\$ 6,000}{100}$ (100) = $6,000
Present year	$12,000	200	$\frac{\$12,000}{200}$ (100) = $6,000

The income of another wage earner increased from $7,000 in 1963 to $8,000 in 1969. Assume that the Consumer Price Index in 1963 was 140 (1957–59 = 100) and that the CPI was 200 in 1969. The wage earner's real, or deflated, income in 1963 was _____ and _____ in 1969. Indicate what happened to his buying power (real income) from 1963 to 1969. Interpret. _____
_____. The same concept is used to determine the real sales of a company.

$5,000 found by [$7,000/ 140](100)

$4,000 found by [$8,000/ 200](100)

His real income decreased $1,000, or 20 percent, from 1963 to 1969 indicating that he can buy less in 1969 than he did in 1963.

17

Purchasing power of the dollar

The Consumer Price Index is also used to determine the *purchasing power of the dollar*. Again, assume that the CPI is 200 at the present time (1957–59 = 100). Thus, prices have doubled from the base period to the present. Another way of stating this is that the purchasing power of the dollar has been cut in half. Thus, the purchasing power of the dollar today, based on prices in the latter part of the 1950's, is only $0.50 (computed by dividing $1 by 200 and multiplying the answer by 100).

Suppose that the Consumer Price Index was 125.0 in 1968 (1957–59 = 100). What was the purchasing power of the dollar in 1968 based on prices in the latter part of the 1950's? _____. What is the basic reason for the decline in the purchasing power of a dollar in a period of approximately 10 years? _____
_____

$0.80

Prices increased 25 percent during the period 1957–59 to 1968. Thus, the dollar in 1968 was worth only 80 cents compared with a dollar in the latter part of the 1950's.

Final Self-Review Examination

First, answer all of the questions. Then check your answers against those given at the end of this chapter. Scoring: 10 problems × 10 points each = 100 possible points.

18. Assume that the Index of Industrial Production was 109.2 for January 1969. (1957–59 = 100.) The base period is (*a*)_____.
The base number index is (*b*)_____.
The index of 109.2 indicates that when all pro-

duction was combined, it (increased/decreased) (*c*)_____ during a period of about (*d*)_____ years.

19. Give two reasons why index numbers are compiled and published.
(1)_____
_____
(2)_____
_____

20. Determine the unweighted price index, (simple index) (price relative) for 1969 based on 1961 (see the following table). (a)_____

Year	Ton Price of Iron Ore
1961	$18
1962	22
1969	54

Interpret the index for 1969 (1961 = 100) (b)_____

If 1961–62 were used as the base period, the price relative for 1969 would be (c)_____

Questions 21, 22, and 23 are based on the following table.

Item	1966 Price	1966 Amount Consumed	1969 Price	1969 Amount Consumed
Oil (barrel)	$ 4	100	5	200
Wool cloth (yard)	2	1,000	2	2,000
Steel (ton)	20	50	15	100

21. Using the Laspeyres method, the weighted index of price is _____ for 1969 (1966 = 100).

22. Using the Laspeyres method, the weighted index of quantity is _____ for 1969 (1966 = 100).

23. The index of value for 1969 based on 1966 is (a)_____, indicating that the value of these items (increased/decreased) (b)_____ about (c)_____ percent from 1966 to 1969.

24. A statistician wishes to design a special-purpose index to measure general business activity in the United States. The base period is to be 1960. In his judgment, the industrial production should be weighted 40, department store sales 30, employment 20, and money turnover (a)_____. Determine the special purpose index of general business activity for 1969. (b)_____

	1960 = 100			
Year	Index of Industrial Production	Index of Department Store Sales	Index of Employment	Index of Money Turnover
1969	180	90	103	210

25. Indicate two criteria for the construction of an index.

26. The price changes in meats and vegetables from 1965 to 1969 are to be compared. However, the two price indexes are on different bases, making a comparison difficult. Shift the bases and make a comparison of the two price changes from 1965 to 1969.

Year	Index of the Price of Meats 1957 = 100	Index of the Price of Vegetables 1961 = 100
1965	150	120
1969	180	132

The Index of Meat Prices for 1969 (1965 = 100) is (a)_____ and the Index of Vegetable Prices for 1969 (1965 = 100) is (b)_____. A comparison of them indicates that (c)_____.

27. The Consumer Price Index and the money income of Mr. Smith for the years 1961, 1962 and 1969 follow.

Year	Consumer Price Index 1957–59 = 100	Mr. Smith's Income
1961	110	$4,300
1962	120	4,800
1969	144	7,200

Based on 1957–59, Mr. Smith's real income for 1969 was (a) $_____. His real income in 1962 was (b) $_____. A comparison of the two real incomes indicates that (c)_____

_____

_____

_____

Based on the Consumer Price Index given, the purchasing power in 1969 was (d) $_____ _____ (1957–59 = 100). This indicates that if Mr. Absent-Minded misplaced $1,000 sometime between 1957 and 1959, and found it in 1969, the $1,000 could only purchase (e) $_____ worth of goods.

Answers to Final Self-Review Examination

18. (a) an average of 1957, 1958, and 1959
    (b) 100
    (c) increased
    (d) 11

19. (In any order.) Indexes facilitate a comparison of unlike series such as production, employment, and sales. When the numbers being compared or analyzed are large (such as total department store sales), it is easier, and more meaningful, to compare percent changes.

20. (a) 300
    (b) Price of iron ore increased 200 percent from 1961 to 1969.
    (c) 270

21. [$3,250/$3,400](100) = 95.6

22. [$6,800/$3,400](100) = 200.0

23. (a) [$6,500/$3,400](100) = 191.2
    (b) increased
    (c) 91.2

24. (a) 10
    (b) 140.6

25. (In any order.) The base year, or years, should be somewhat normal. The base period should not be too far in the past, or too close to the present year. Consideration should be given to the items to be included in the index and the weight placed on each.

26. (a) 120
    (b) 110
    (c) Meat prices increased 20 percent from 1965 compared with a 10 percent increase in vegetable prices during the same period.

27. (a) $5,000
    (b) $4,000
    (c) Although his money income increased $2,400 ($7,200 − $4,800), Mr. Smith's real income only increased $1,000 ($5,000 − $4,000). This indicates, however, that his money income increased at a more rapid rate than prices (as measured by the CPI) resulting in a gain in his standard of living.
    (d) 69.4 cents
    (e) $694

Glossary of Terms and Formulas

Arithmetic Mean ($\overline{X}$)

Ungrouped data: $\overline{X} = \dfrac{\Sigma X}{n}$

Grouped data: $\overline{X} = \dfrac{\Sigma f X}{n}$

The arithmetic average is the sum of all the observations divided by the total number of observations (Chapter 4).

Average Deviation (A.D. or M.D.)

Ungrouped data: A.D. $= \dfrac{\Sigma |X - \overline{X}|}{n}$

It is also called the *Mean Deviation*. The average deviation is the average of the absolute deviations from the mean, i.e., all deviations from the mean are considered positive (Chapter 5).

Bayes' Rule

$$P(B_i|A) = \frac{P(B_i) \cdot P(A|B_i)}{\sum_i P(B_i) \cdot P(A|B_i)}$$

It is a theorem (formula) for determining the posterior probability $P(B_i|A)$. This is accomplished by revising the prior probability B_i given that event A has occurred. There may be more than one prior probability. The large sigma indicates that all probabilities are to be summed given occurrence A (Chapter 12).

Chi-Square (χ^2)

$$\chi^2 = \sum \frac{(f_o - f_e)^2}{f_e}$$

One use of the statistic chi-square is testing the hypothesis that one set of observed frequencies is significantly different from an expected set of frequencies (Chapter 13).

Confidence Limits

For Variables: $\overline{X} \pm z(s_{\bar{x}})$

For Proportions: $p \pm z(s_p)$

Based on sample data, the confidence limits are two values between which the population mean (or proportion) will fall given a certain level of confidence—such as the 0.95 level (Chapter 9).

Correlation, Coefficient of (r or R)

$$r = \frac{n(\Sigma XY) - (\Sigma X)(\Sigma Y)}{\sqrt{[n(\Sigma X^2) - (\Sigma X)^2][n(\Sigma Y^2) - (\Sigma Y)^2]}}$$

r is the simple coefficient of correlation. It measures the degree of relationship between a dependent variable Y and an independent variable X. In multiple correlation, R gives the degree of relationship between Y and $X_1, X_2 \ldots X_n$ (Chapters 15, 16).

Determination, Coefficient of (r^2 or R^2)

It is the coefficient of correlation squared. (See correlation coefficient for formula.) The coefficient of determination r in simple correlation analysis measures the percent of the variation in Y (the dependent variable) explained by X (the independent variable). In multiple correlation analysis, R^2 measures the percent variation in Y explained by the X's ($X_1, X_2 \ldots X_n$ (Chapter 15, 16).

Finite Multiplier

Computed by: $\sqrt{\dfrac{N - n}{N - 1}}$

The finite multiplier is also called the finite correction factor. It is applied to the standard error of the mean $s_{\bar{x}}$, or the standard error of the proportion s_p, in a sampling problem. It compensates for the size of the sample n relative to the size of the finite population N (Chapter 9).

Geometric Mean (G.M.)

G.M. $= \sqrt[n]{X_1 \cdot X_2 \cdot X_3 \ldots X_n}$

It is defined as the nth root of the product of all of the observations in the series. It is usually computed using logarithms. A useful formula for finding the geometric mean increase in sales, production, etc. from one period of time to another is:

$$G.M. = \sqrt[n-1]{\frac{\text{Value at end of period}}{\text{Value at beginning of period}}} - 1$$

(Chapter 4).

Index

As an example, a weighted price index can be found by:

$$P = \frac{\Sigma p_n q_o}{\Sigma p_o q_o} (100)$$

There are price, quality, value and special-purpose indexes. Expressed as a percent, an index can be used to measure the percent change in one item, or a composite of items, from one period of time (designated as the base) to another period of time (Chapter 18).

Median

$$\text{Median} = L_2 + \frac{\frac{n}{2} - CF_2}{f} (i)$$

The observations are first arranged from low to high or vice versa. The median is the point above which and below which half of the observations lie (Chapter 4).

Mode

$$\text{Mode} = L_1 + \frac{\Delta_1}{\Delta_1 + \Delta_2} (i)$$

It is defined as the value of the most frequently occurring item (Chapter 4).

Nondetermination, Coefficient of (k^2 or $1 - r^2$ or $1 - R^2$)

(See correlation coefficient for formula for r.) It is the percent of the variation in the dependent variable Y not explained by the one independent variable X in simple correlation analysis. In multiple correlation analysis, $1 - R^2$ is a measure of the percent variation in Y not explained by the many independent variables $X_1, X_2 \ldots X_n$ (Chapters 15, 16).

Purchasing Power of the Dollar

$$\text{Computed by: } \frac{\$1}{\text{CPI}} (100)$$

It is the reciprocal of the Consumer Price Index and expresses the current value of a dollar in relation to the base period of the index. If the base of the index was 1957–59 and the purchasing power of the dollar for the current month was \$0.85, it indicates that the 1957–59 dollar is now worth only 85 cents. (Chapter 18).

Quartile Deviation (Q.D.)

$$\text{Q.D.} = \frac{Q_3 - Q_1}{2}$$

It is also called the Semi-Interquartile Range. The quartile deviation is defined as half of the distance between the third and the first quartile (Chapter 5).

Range (R)

It is the distance between the highest and lowest value (Chapter 5).

Real Wages

$$\text{Computed by: } \frac{\$ \text{ Wages}}{\text{Consumer Price Index}} (100)$$

Real wages, or real income, of an individual represents the dollar value of goods and services a wage earner can buy currently compared with the amount he could purchase in the base period of the index (Chapter 18).

Skewness, Coefficient of (Sk)

$$Sk = \frac{3(\bar{X} - \text{median})}{s}$$

Developed by Karl Pearson, the coefficient of skewness is a relative measure which reveals the degree and the direction (plus or minus) of the skewness of a frequency distribution. There are other similar measures (Chapter 5).

Standard Deviation (s or σ)

$$\text{Ungrouped data: } s = \sqrt{\frac{\Sigma X^2}{n} - \bar{X}^2}$$

$$\text{Grouped data: } s = \sqrt{\frac{\Sigma f X^2}{n} - \bar{X}^2}$$

The standard deviation is the square root of the sum of the squared deviations from the mean divided by the number of observations. It is the most commonly used measure to describe the dispersion in a normal distribution (Chapter 5).

Variance (s^2 or σ^2)

It is the standard deviation squared. See: Standard deviation for formula (Chapter 5).

Variation, Coefficient of (CV)

$$CV = \frac{s}{\bar{X}}(100)$$

It is a percent found by dividing the standard deviation of a distribution by its mean. It expresses the variation in relative terms, thus facilitating a comparison of the dispersion of two or more frequency distributions (Chapter 5).

z Value (z)

For two means:

$$z = \frac{\bar{X}_1 - \bar{X}_2}{\sqrt{\left(\frac{s_1}{\sqrt{n_1}}\right)^2 + \left(\frac{s_2}{\sqrt{n_2}}\right)^2}}$$

For two proportions:

$$z = \frac{p_1 - p_2}{\sqrt{\frac{\bar{P}(1 - \bar{P})}{n_1} + \frac{\bar{P}(1 - \bar{P})}{n_2}}}$$

One use of the z value is in testing a hypothesis involving the difference between two means or two proportions. A hypothesis is stated that two samples are from two identical populations or the same population. If the hypothesis is true, then the distribution of z values of many paired samples will approximate a normal distribution with a mean of zero (Chapter 10).

Appendix I. Logarithms

N	0	1	2	3	4	5	6	7	8	9
10	0000	0043	0086	0128	0170	0212	0253	0294	0334	0374
11	0414	0453	0492	0531	0569	0607	0645	0682	0719	0755
12	0792	0828	0864	0899	0934	0969	1004	1038	1072	1106
13	1139	1173	1206	1239	1271	1303	1335	1367	1399	1430
14	1461	1492	1523	1553	1584	1614	1644	1673	1703	1732
15	1761	1790	1818	1847	1875	1903	1931	1959	1987	2014
16	2041	2068	2095	2122	2148	2175	2201	2227	2253	2279
17	2304	2330	2355	2380	2405	2430	2455	2480	2504	2529
18	2553	2577	2601	2625	2648	2672	2695	2718	2742	2765
19	2788	2810	2833	2856	2878	2900	2923	2945	2967	2989
20	3010	3032	3054	3075	3096	3118	3139	3160	3181	3201
21	3222	3243	3263	3284	3304	3324	3345	3365	3385	3404
22	3424	3444	3464	3483	3502	3522	3541	3560	3579	3598
23	3617	3636	3655	3674	3692	3711	3729	3747	3766	3784
24	3802	3820	3838	3856	3874	3892	3909	3927	3945	3962
25	3979	3997	4014	4031	4048	4065	4082	4099	4116	4133
26	4150	4166	4183	4200	4216	4232	4249	4265	4281	4298
27	4314	4330	4346	4362	4378	4393	4409	4425	4440	4456
28	4472	4487	4502	4518	4533	4548	4564	4579	4594	4609
29	4624	4639	4654	4669	4683	4698	4713	4728	4742	4757
30	4771	4786	4800	4814	4829	4843	4857	4871	4886	4900
31	4914	4928	4942	4955	4969	4983	4997	5011	5024	5038
32	5051	5065	5079	5092	5105	5119	5132	5145	5159	5172
33	5185	5198	5211	5224	5237	5250	5263	5276	5289	5302
34	5315	5328	5340	5353	5366	5378	5391	5403	5416	5428
35	5441	5453	5465	5478	5490	5502	5514	5527	5539	5551
36	5563	5575	5587	5599	5611	5623	5635	5647	5658	5670
37	5682	5694	5705	5717	5729	5740	5752	5763	5775	5786
38	5798	5809	5821	5832	5843	5855	5866	5877	5888	5899
39	5911	5922	5933	5944	5955	5966	5977	5988	5999	6010
40	6021	6031	6042	6053	6064	6075	6085	6096	6107	6117
41	6128	6138	6149	6160	6170	6180	6191	6201	6212	6222
42	6232	6243	6253	6263	6274	6284	6294	6304	6314	6325
43	6335	6345	6355	6365	6375	6385	6395	6405	6415	6425
44	6435	6444	6454	6464	6474	6484	6493	6503	6513	6522
45	6532	6542	6551	6561	6571	6580	6590	6599	6609	6618
46	6628	6637	6646	6656	6665	6675	6684	6693	6702	6712
47	6721	6730	6739	6749	6758	6767	6776	6785	6794	6803
48	6812	6821	6830	6839	6848	6857	6866	6875	6884	6893
49	6902	6911	6920	6928	6937	6946	6955	6964	6972	6981
50	6990	6998	7007	7016	7024	7033	7042	7050	7059	7067
51	7076	7084	7093	7101	7110	7118	7126	7135	7143	7152
52	7160	7168	7177	7185	7193	7202	7210	7218	7226	7235
53	7243	7251	7259	7267	7275	7284	7292	7300	7308	7316
54	7324	7332	7340	7348	7356	7364	7372	7380	7388	7396

N	0	1	2	3	4	5	6	7	8	9
55	7404	7412	7419	7427	7435	7443	7451	7459	7466	7474
56	7482	7490	7497	7505	7513	7520	7528	7536	7543	7551
57	7559	7566	7574	7582	7589	7597	7604	7612	7619	7627
58	7634	7642	7649	7657	7664	7672	7679	7686	7694	7701
59	7709	7716	7723	7731	7738	7745	7752	7760	7767	7774
60	7782	7789	7796	7803	7810	7818	7825	7832	7839	7846
61	7853	7860	7868	7875	7882	7889	7896	7903	7910	7917
62	7924	7931	7938	7945	7952	7959	7966	7973	7980	7987
63	7993	8000	8007	8014	8021	8028	8035	8041	8048	8055
64	8062	8069	8075	8082	8089	8096	8102	8109	8116	8122
65	8129	8136	8142	8149	8156	8162	8169	8176	8182	8189
66	8195	8202	8209	8215	8222	8228	8235	8241	8248	8254
67	8261	8267	8274	8280	8287	8293	8299	8306	8312	8319
68	8325	8331	8338	8344	8351	8357	8363	8370	8376	8382
69	8388	8395	8401	8407	8414	8420	8426	8432	8439	8445
70	8451	8457	8463	8470	8476	8482	8488	8494	8500	8506
71	8513	8519	8525	8531	8537	8543	8549	8555	8561	8567
72	8573	8579	8585	8591	8597	8603	8609	8615	8621	8627
73	8633	8639	8645	8651	8657	8663	8669	8675	8681	8686
74	8692	8698	8704	8710	8716	8722	8727	8733	8739	8745
75	8751	8756	8762	8768	8774	8779	8785	8791	8797	8802
76	8808	8814	8820	8825	8831	8837	8842	8848	8854	8859
77	8865	8871	8876	8882	8887	8893	8899	8904	8910	8915
78	8921	8927	8932	8938	8943	8949	8954	8960	8965	8971
79	8976	8982	8987	8993	8998	9004	9009	9015	9020	9025
80	9031	9036	9042	9047	9053	9058	9063	9069	9074	9079
81	9085	9090	9096	9101	9106	9112	9117	9122	9128	9133
82	9138	9143	9149	9154	9159	9165	9170	9175	9180	9186
83	9191	9196	9201	9206	9212	9217	9222	9227	9232	9238
84	9243	9248	9253	9258	9263	9269	9274	9279	9284	9289
85	9294	9299	9304	9309	9315	9320	9325	9330	9335	9340
86	9345	9350	9355	9360	9365	9370	9375	9380	9385	9390
87	9395	9400	9405	9410	9415	9420	9425	9430	9435	9440
88	9445	9450	9455	9460	9465	9469	9474	9479	9484	9489
89	9494	9499	9504	9509	9513	9518	9523	9528	9533	9538
90	9542	9547	9552	9557	9562	9566	9571	9576	9581	9586
91	9590	9595	9600	9605	9609	9614	9619	9624	9628	9633
92	9638	9643	9647	9652	9657	9661	9666	9671	9675	9680
93	9685	9689	9694	9699	9703	9708	9713	9717	9722	9727
94	9731	9736	9741	9745	9750	9754	9759	9763	9768	9773
95	9777	9782	9786	9791	9795	9800	9805	9809	9814	9818
96	9823	9827	9832	9836	9841	9845	9850	9854	9859	9863
97	9868	9872	9877	9881	9886	9890	9894	9899	9903	9908
98	9912	9917	9921	9926	9930	9934	9939	9943	9948	9952
99	9956	9961	9965	9969	9974	9978	9983	9987	9991	9996

Appendix II. Factors for Control Charts

Number of Items in Sample, n	Chart for Averages — Factors for Control Limits, A_2	Chart for Ranges — Factors for Central Line, d_2	Chart for Ranges — Factors for Control Limits, D_3	Chart for Ranges — Factors for Control Limits, D_4
2	1.880	1.128	0	3.267
3	1.023	1.693	0	2.575
4	.729	2.059	0	2.282
5	.577	2.326	0	2.115
6	.483	2.534	0	2.004
7	.419	2.704	.076	1.924
8	.373	2.847	.136	1.864
9	.337	2.970	.184	1.816
10	.308	3.078	.223	1.777
11	.285	3.173	.256	1.744
12	.266	3.258	.284	1.716
13	.249	3.336	.308	1.692
14	.235	3.407	.329	1.671
15	.223	3.472	.348	1.652

Source: Adapted from American Society for Testing and Materials, *Manual on Quality Control of Materials*, 1951, Table B2, p. 115. For a more detailed table and explanation, see Acheson J. Duncan, *Quality Control and Industrial Statistics* (3rd ed.; Homewood, Ill.: Richard D. Irwin, Inc., 1965) Table M, p. 927.

Appendix III. Square Roots*

n	$\sqrt{n}$	$\sqrt{10n}$
1.00	1.00000	3.16228
1.01	1.00499	3.17805
1.02	1.00995	3.19374
1.03	1.01489	3.20936
1.04	1.01980	3.22490
1.05	1.02470	3.24037
1.06	1.02956	3.25576
1.07	1.03441	3.27109
1.08	1.03923	3.28634
1.09	1.04403	3.30151
1.10	1.04881	3.31662
1.11	1.05357	3.33167
1.12	1.05830	3.34664
1.13	1.06301	3.36155
1.14	1.06771	3.37639
1.15	1.07238	3.39116
1.16	1.07703	3.40588
1.17	1.08167	3.42053
1.18	1.08628	3.43511
1.19	1.09087	3.44964
1.20	1.09545	3.46410
1.21	1.10000	3.47851
1.22	1.10454	3.49285
1.23	1.10905	3.50714
1.24	1.11355	3.52136
1.25	1.11803	3.53553
1.26	1.12250	3.54965
1.27	1.12694	3.56371
1.28	1.13137	3.57771
1.29	1.13578	3.59166
1.30	1.14018	3.60555
1.31	1.14455	3.61939
1.32	1.14891	3.63318
1.33	1.15326	3.64692
1.34	1.15758	3.66060
1.35	1.16190	3.67423
1.36	1.16619	3.68782
1.37	1.17047	3.70135
1.38	1.17473	3.71484
1.39	1.17898	3.72827
1.40	1.18322	3.74166
1.41	1.18743	3.75500
1.42	1.19164	3.76829
1.43	1.19583	3.78153
1.44	1.20000	3.79473
1.45	1.20416	3.80789
1.46	1.20830	3.82099
1.47	1.21244	3.83406
1.48	1.21655	3.84708
1.49	1.22066	3.86005

n	$\sqrt{n}$	$\sqrt{10n}$
1.50	1.22474	3.87298
1.51	1.22882	3.88587
1.52	1.23288	3.89872
1.53	1.23693	3.91152
1.54	1.24097	3.92428
1.55	1.24499	3.93700
1.56	1.24900	3.94968
1.57	1.25300	3.96232
1.58	1.25698	3.97492
1.59	1.26095	3.98748
1.60	1.26491	4.00000
1.61	1.26886	4.01248
1.62	1.27279	4.02492
1.63	1.27671	4.03733
1.64	1.28062	4.04969
1.65	1.28452	4.06202
1.66	1.28841	4.07431
1.67	1.29228	4.08656
1.68	1.29615	4.09878
1.69	1.30000	4.11096
1.70	1.30384	4.12311
1.71	1.30767	4.13521
1.72	1.31149	4.14729
1.73	1.31529	4.15933
1.74	1.31909	4.17133
1.75	1.32288	4.18330
1.76	1.32665	4.19524
1.77	1.33041	4.20714
1.78	1.33417	4.21900
1.79	1.33791	4.23084
1.80	1.34164	4.24264
1.81	1.34536	4.25441
1.82	1.34907	4.26615
1.83	1.35277	4.27785
1.84	1.35647	4.28952
1.85	1.36015	4.30116
1.86	1.36382	4.31277
1.87	1.36748	4.32435
1.88	1.37113	4.33590
1.89	1.37477	4.34741
1.90	1.37840	4.35890
1.91	1.38203	4.37035
1.92	1.38564	4.38178
1.93	1.38924	4.39318
1.94	1.39284	4.40454
1.95	1.39642	4.41588
1.96	1.40000	4.42719
1.97	1.40357	4.43847
1.98	1.40712	4.44972
1.99	1.41067	4.46094

n	$\sqrt{n}$	$\sqrt{10n}$
2.00	1.41421	4.47214
2.01	1.41774	4.48330
2.02	1.42127	4.49444
2.03	1.42478	4.50555
2.04	1.42829	4.51664
2.05	1.43178	4.52769
2.06	1.43527	4.53872
2.07	1.43875	4.54973
2.08	1.44222	4.56070
2.09	1.44568	4.57165
2.10	1.44914	4.58258
2.11	1.45258	4.59347
2.12	1.45602	4.60435
2.13	1.45945	4.61519
2.14	1.46287	4.62601
2.15	1.46629	4.63681
2.16	1.46969	4.64758
2.17	1.47309	4.65833
2.18	1.47648	4.66905
2.19	1.47986	4.67974
2.20	1.48324	4.69042
2.21	1.48661	4.70106
2.22	1.48997	4.71169
2.23	1.49332	4.72229
2.24	1.49666	4.73286
2.25	1.50000	4.74342
2.26	1.50333	4.75395
2.27	1.50665	4.76445
2.28	1.50997	4.77493
2.29	1.51327	4.78539
2.30	1.51658	4.79583
2.31	1.51987	4.80625
2.32	1.52315	4.81664
2.33	1.52643	4.82701
2.34	1.52971	4.83735
2.35	1.53297	4.84768
2.36	1.53623	4.85798
2.37	1.53948	4.86826
2.38	1.54272	4.87852
2.39	1.54596	4.88876
2.40	1.54919	4.89898
2.41	1.55242	4.90918
2.42	1.55563	4.91935
2.43	1.55885	4.92950
2.44	1.56205	4.93964
2.45	1.56525	4.94975
2.46	1.56844	4.95984
2.47	1.57162	4.96991
2.48	1.57480	4.97996
2.49	1.57797	4.98999

n	$\sqrt{n}$	$\sqrt{10n}$
2.50	1.58114	5.00000
2.51	1.58430	5.00999
2.52	1.58745	5.01996
2.53	1.59060	5.02991
2.54	1.59374	5.03984
2.55	1.59687	5.04975
2.56	1.60000	5.05964
2.57	1.60312	5.06952
2.58	1.60624	5.07937
2.59	1.60935	5.08920
2.60	1.61245	5.09902
2.61	1.61555	5.10882
2.62	1.61864	5.11859
2.63	1.62173	5.12835
2.64	1.62481	5.13809
2.65	1.62788	5.14782
2.66	1.63095	5.15752
2.67	1.63401	5.16720
2.68	1.63707	5.17687
2.69	1.64012	5.18652
2.70	1.64317	5.19615
2.71	1.64621	5.20577
2.72	1.64924	5.21536
2.73	1.65227	5.22494
2.74	1.65529	5.23450
2.75	1.65831	5.24404
2.76	1.66132	5.25357
2.77	1.66433	5.26308
2.78	1.66733	5.27257
2.79	1.67033	5.28205
2.80	1.67332	5.29150
2.81	1.67631	5.30094
2.82	1.67929	5.31037
2.83	1.68226	5.31977
2.84	1.68523	5.32917
2.85	1.68819	5.33854
2.86	1.69115	5.34790
2.87	1.69411	5.35724
2.88	1.69706	5.36656
2.89	1.70000	5.37587
2.90	1.70294	5.38516
2.91	1.70587	5.39444
2.92	1.70880	5.40370
2.93	1.71172	5.41295
2.94	1.71464	5.42218
2.95	1.71756	5.43139
2.96	1.72047	5.44059
2.97	1.72337	5.44977
2.98	1.72627	5.45894
2.99	1.72916	5.46809

n	$\sqrt{n}$	$\sqrt{10n}$
3.00	1.73205	5.47723
3.01	1.73494	5.48635
3.02	1.73781	5.49545
3.03	1.74069	5.50454
3.04	1.74356	5.51362
3.05	1.74642	5.52268
3.06	1.74929	5.53173
3.07	1.75214	5.54076
3.08	1.75499	5.54977
3.09	1.75784	5.55878
3.10	1.76068	5.56776
3.11	1.76352	5.57674
3.12	1.76635	5.58570
3.13	1.76918	5.59464
3.14	1.77200	5.60357
3.15	1.77482	5.61249
3.16	1.77764	5.62139
3.17	1.78045	5.63028
3.18	1.78326	5.63915
3.19	1.78606	5.64801
3.20	1.78885	5.65685
3.21	1.79165	5.66569
3.22	1.79444	5.67450
3.23	1.79722	5.68331
3.24	1.80000	5.69210
3.25	1.80278	5.70088
3.26	1.80555	5.70964
3.27	1.80831	5.71839
3.28	1.81108	5.72713
3.29	1.81384	5.73585
3.30	1.81659	5.74456
3.31	1.81934	5.75326
3.32	1.82209	5.76194
3.33	1.82483	5.77062
3.34	1.82757	5.77927
3.35	1.83030	5.78792
3.36	1.83303	5.79655
3.37	1.83576	5.80517
3.38	1.83848	5.81378
3.39	1.84120	5.82237
3.40	1.84391	5.83095
3.41	1.84662	5.83952
3.42	1.84932	5.84808
3.43	1.85203	5.85662
3.44	1.85472	5.86515
3.45	1.85742	5.87367
3.46	1.86011	5.88218
3.47	1.86279	5.89067
3.48	1.86548	5.89915
3.49	1.86815	5.90762

n	$\sqrt{n}$	$\sqrt{10n}$
3.50	1.87083	5.91608
3.51	1.87350	5.92453
3.52	1.87617	5.93296
3.53	1.87883	5.94138
3.54	1.88149	5.94979
3.55	1.88414	5.95819
3.56	1.88680	5.96657
3.57	1.88944	5.97495
3.58	1.89209	5.98331
3.59	1.89473	5.99166
3.60	1.89737	6.00000
3.61	1.90000	6.00833
3.62	1.90263	6.01664
3.63	1.90526	6.02495
3.64	1.90788	6.03324
3.65	1.91050	6.04152
3.66	1.91311	6.04979
3.67	1.91572	6.05805
3.68	1.91833	6.06630
3.69	1.92094	6.07454
3.70	1.92354	6.08276
3.71	1.92614	6.09098
3.72	1.92873	6.09918
3.73	1.93132	6.10737
3.74	1.93391	6.11555
3.75	1.93649	6.12372
3.76	1.93907	6.13188
3.77	1.94165	6.14003
3.78	1.94422	6.14817
3.79	1.94679	6.15630
3.80	1.94936	6.16441
3.81	1.95192	6.17252
3.82	1.95448	6.18061
3.83	1.95704	6.18870
3.84	1.95959	6.19677
3.85	1.96214	6.20484
3.86	1.96469	6.21289
3.87	1.96723	6.22093
3.88	1.96977	6.22896
3.89	1.97231	6.23699
3.90	1.97484	6.24500
3.91	1.97737	6.25300
3.92	1.97990	6.26099
3.93	1.98242	6.26897
3.94	1.98494	6.27694
3.95	1.98746	6.28490
3.96	1.98997	6.29285
3.97	1.99249	6.30079
3.98	1.99499	6.30872
3.99	1.99750	6.31664

* Adapted with permission of the publisher from *Macmillan Selected Mathematical Tables* by Earle R. Hedrick. Copyright 1936 by The Macmillan Company.

n	√n	√10n	n	√n	√10n	n	√n	√10n
4.00	2.00000	6.32456	4.50	2.12132	6.70820	5.00	2.23607	7.07107
4.01	2.00250	6.33246	4.51	2.12368	6.71565	5.01	2.23830	7.07814
4.02	2.00499	6.34035	4.52	2.12603	6.72309	5.02	2.24054	7.08520
4.03	2.00749	6.34823	4.53	2.12838	6.73053	5.03	2.24277	7.09225
4.04	2.00998	6.35610	4.54	2.13073	6.73795	5.04	2.24499	7.09930
4.05	2.01246	6.36396	4.55	2.13307	6.74537	5.05	2.24722	7.10634
4.06	2.01494	6.37181	4.56	2.13542	6.75278	5.06	2.24944	7.11337
4.07	2.01742	6.37966	4.57	2.13776	6.76018	5.07	2.25167	7.12039
4.08	2.01990	6.38749	4.58	2.14009	6.76757	5.08	2.25389	7.12741
4.09	2.02237	6.39531	4.59	2.14243	6.77495	5.09	2.25610	7.13442
4.10	2.02485	6.40312	4.60	2.14476	6.78233	5.10	2.25832	7.14143
4.11	2.02731	6.41093	4.61	2.14709	6.78970	5.11	2.26053	7.14843
4.12	2.02978	6.41872	4.62	2.14942	6.79706	5.12	2.26274	7.15542
4.13	2.03224	6.42651	4.63	2.15174	6.80441	5.13	2.26495	7.16240
4.14	2.03470	6.43428	4.64	2.15407	6.81175	5.14	2.26716	7.16938
4.15	2.03715	6.44205	4.65	2.15639	6.81909	5.15	2.26936	7.17635
4.16	2.03961	6.44981	4.66	2.15870	6.82642	5.16	2.27156	7.18331
4.17	2.04206	6.45755	4.67	2.16102	6.83374	5.17	2.27376	7.19027
4.18	2.04450	6.46529	4.68	2.16333	6.84105	5.18	2.27596	7.19722
4.19	2.04695	6.47302	4.69	2.16564	6.84836	5.19	2.27816	7.20417
4.20	2.04939	6.48074	4.70	2.16795	6.85565	5.20	2.28035	7.21110
4.21	2.05183	6.48845	4.71	2.17025	6.86294	5.21	2.28254	7.21803
4.22	2.05426	6.49615	4.72	2.17256	6.87023	5.22	2.28473	7.22496
4.23	2.05670	6.50384	4.73	2.17486	6.87750	5.23	2.28692	7.23187
4.24	2.05913	6.51153	4.74	2.17715	6.88477	5.24	2.28910	7.23878
4.25	2.06155	6.51920	4.75	2.17945	6.89202	5.25	2.29129	7.24569
4.26	2.06398	6.52687	4.76	2.18174	6.89928	5.26	2.29347	7.25259
4.27	2.06640	6.53452	4.77	2.18403	6.90652	5.27	2.29565	7.25948
4.28	2.06882	6.54217	4.78	2.18632	6.91375	5.28	2.29783	7.26636
4.29	2.07123	6.54981	4.79	2.18861	6.92098	5.29	2.30000	7.27324
4.30	2.07364	6.55744	4.80	2.19089	6.92820	5.30	2.30217	7.28011
4.31	2.07605	6.56506	4.81	2.19317	6.93542	5.31	2.30434	7.28697
4.32	2.07846	6.57267	4.82	2.19545	6.94262	5.32	2.30651	7.29383
4.33	2.08087	6.58027	4.83	2.19773	6.94982	5.33	2.30868	7.30068
4.34	2.08327	6.58787	4.84	2.20000	6.95701	5.34	2.31084	7.30753
4.35	2.08567	6.59545	4.85	2.20227	6.96419	5.35	2.31301	7.31437
4.36	2.08806	6.60303	4.86	2.20454	6.97137	5.36	2.31517	7.32120
4.37	2.09045	6.61060	4.87	2.20681	6.97854	5.37	2.31733	7.32803
4.38	2.09284	6.61816	4.88	2.20907	6.98570	5.38	2.31948	7.33485
4.39	2.09523	6.62571	4.89	2.21133	6.99285	5.39	2.32164	7.34166
4.40	2.09762	6.63325	4.90	2.21359	7.00000	5.40	2.32379	7.34847
4.41	2.10000	6.64078	4.91	2.21585	7.00714	5.41	2.32594	7.35527
4.42	2.10238	6.64831	4.92	2.21811	7.01427	5.42	2.32809	7.36206
4.43	2.10476	6.65582	4.93	2.22036	7.02140	5.43	2.33024	7.36885
4.44	2.10713	6.66333	4.94	2.22261	7.02851	5.44	2.33238	7.37564
4.45	2.10950	6.67083	4.95	2.22486	7.03562	5.45	2.33452	7.38241
4.46	2.11187	6.67832	4.96	2.22711	7.04273	5.46	2.33666	7.38918
4.47	2.11424	6.68581	4.97	2.22935	7.04982	5.47	2.33880	7.39594
4.48	2.11660	6.69328	4.98	2.23159	7.05691	5.48	2.34094	7.40270
4.49	2.11896	6.70075	4.99	2.23383	7.06399	5.49	2.34307	7.40945

n	√n	√10n	n	√n	√10n	n	√n	√10n
5.50	2.34521	7.41620	6.00	2.44949	7.74597	6.50	2.54951	8.06226
5.51	2.34734	7.42294	6.01	2.45153	7.75242	6.51	2.55147	8.06846
5.52	2.34947	7.42967	6.02	2.45357	7.75887	6.52	2.55343	8.07465
5.53	2.35160	7.43640	6.03	2.45561	7.76531	6.53	2.55539	8.08084
5.54	2.35372	7.44312	6.04	2.45764	7.77174	6.54	2.55734	8.08703
5.55	2.35584	7.44983	6.05	2.45967	7.77817	6.55	2.55930	8.09321
5.56	2.35797	7.45654	6.06	2.46171	7.78460	6.56	2.56125	8.09938
5.57	2.36008	7.46324	6.07	2.46374	7.79102	6.57	2.56320	8.10555
5.58	2.36220	7.46994	6.08	2.46577	7.79744	6.58	2.56515	8.11172
5.59	2.36432	7.47663	6.09	2.46779	7.80385	6.59	2.56710	8.11788
5.60	2.36643	7.48331	6.10	2.46982	7.81025	6.60	2.56905	8.12404
5.61	2.36854	7.48999	6.11	2.47184	7.81665	6.61	2.57099	8.13019
5.62	2.37065	7.49667	6.12	2.47386	7.82304	6.62	2.57294	8.13634
5.63	2.37276	7.50333	6.13	2.47588	7.82943	6.63	2.57488	8.14248
5.64	2.37487	7.50999	6.14	2.47790	7.83582	6.64	2.57682	8.14862
5.65	2.37697	7.51665	6.15	2.47992	7.84219	6.65	2.57876	8.15475
5.66	2.37908	7.52330	6.16	2.48193	7.84857	6.66	2.58070	8.16088
5.67	2.38118	7.52994	6.17	2.48395	7.85493	6.67	2.58263	8.16701
5.68	2.38328	7.53658	6.18	2.48596	7.86130	6.68	2.58457	8.17313
5.69	2.38537	7.54321	6.19	2.48797	7.86766	6.69	2.58650	8.17924
5.70	2.38747	7.54983	6.20	2.48998	7.87401	6.70	2.58844	8.18535
5.71	2.38956	7.55645	6.21	2.49199	7.88036	6.71	2.59037	8.19146
5.72	2.39165	7.56307	6.22	2.49399	7.88670	6.72	2.59230	8.19756
5.73	2.39374	7.56968	6.23	2.49600	7.89303	6.73	2.59422	8.20366
5.74	2.39583	7.57628	6.24	2.49800	7.89937	6.74	2.59615	8.20975
5.75	2.39792	7.58288	6.25	2.50000	7.90569	6.75	2.59808	8.21584
5.76	2.40000	7.58947	6.26	2.50200	7.91202	6.76	2.60000	8.22192
5.77	2.40208	7.59605	6.27	2.50400	7.91833	6.77	2.60192	8.22800
5.78	2.40416	7.60263	6.28	2.50599	7.92465	6.78	2.60384	8.23408
5.79	2.40624	7.60920	6.29	2.50799	7.93095	6.79	2.60576	8.24015
5.80	2.40832	7.61577	6.30	2.50998	7.93725	6.80	2.60768	8.24621
5.81	2.41039	7.62234	6.31	2.51197	7.94355	6.81	2.60960	8.25227
5.82	2.41247	7.62889	6.32	2.51396	7.94984	6.82	2.61151	8.25833
5.83	2.41454	7.63544	6.33	2.51595	7.95613	6.83	2.61343	8.26438
5.84	2.41661	7.64199	6.34	2.51794	7.96241	6.84	2.61534	8.27043
5.85	2.41868	7.64853	6.35	2.51992	7.96869	6.85	2.61725	8.27647
5.86	2.42074	7.65506	6.36	2.52190	7.97496	6.86	2.61916	8.28251
5.87	2.42281	7.66159	6.37	2.52389	7.98123	6.87	2.62107	8.28855
5.88	2.42487	7.66812	6.38	2.52587	7.98749	6.88	2.62298	8.29458
5.89	2.42693	7.67463	6.39	2.52784	7.99375	6.89	2.62488	8.30060
5.90	2.42899	7.68115	6.40	2.52982	8.00000	6.90	2.62679	8.30662
5.91	2.43105	7.68765	6.41	2.53180	8.00625	6.91	2.62869	8.31264
5.92	2.43311	7.69415	6.42	2.53377	8.01249	6.92	2.63059	8.31865
5.93	2.43516	7.70065	6.43	2.53574	8.01873	6.93	2.63249	8.32466
5.94	2.43721	7.70714	6.44	2.53772	8.02496	6.94	2.63439	8.33067
5.95	2.43926	7.71362	6.45	2.53969	8.03119	6.95	2.63629	8.33667
5.96	2.44131	7.72010	6.46	2.54165	8.03741	6.96	2.63818	8.34266
5.97	2.44336	7.72658	6.47	2.54362	8.04363	6.97	2.64008	8.34865
5.98	2.44540	7.73305	6.48	2.54558	8.04984	6.98	2.64197	8.35464
5.99	2.44745	7.73951	6.49	2.54755	8.05605	6.99	2.64386	8.36062

n	√n	√10n	n	√n	√10n	n	√n	√10n	n	√n	√10n	n	√n	√10n	n	√n	√10n
7.00	2.64575	8.36660	7.50	2.73861	8.66025	8.00	2.82843	8.94427	8.50	2.91548	9.21954	9.00	3.00000	9.48683	9.50	3.08221	9.74679
7.01	2.64764	8.37257	7.51	2.74044	8.66603	8.01	2.83019	8.94986	8.51	2.91719	9.22497	9.01	3.00167	9.49210	9.51	3.08383	9.75192
7.02	2.64953	8.37854	7.52	2.74226	8.67179	8.02	2.83196	8.95545	8.52	2.91890	9.23038	9.02	3.00333	9.49737	9.52	3.08545	9.75705
7.03	2.65141	8.38451	7.53	2.74408	8.67756	8.03	2.83373	8.96103	8.53	2.92062	9.23580	9.03	3.00500	9.50263	9.53	3.08707	9.76217
7.04	2.65330	8.39047	7.54	2.74591	8.68332	8.04	2.83549	8.96660	8.54	2.92233	9.24121	9.04	3.00666	9.50789	9.54	3.08869	9.76729
7.05	2.65518	8.39643	7.55	2.74773	8.68907	8.05	2.83725	8.97218	8.55	2.92404	9.24662	9.05	3.00832	9.51315	9.55	3.09031	9.77241
7.06	2.65707	8.40238	7.56	2.74955	8.69483	8.06	2.83901	8.97775	8.56	2.92575	9.25203	9.06	3.00998	9.51840	9.56	3.09192	9.77753
7.07	2.65895	8.40833	7.57	2.75136	8.70057	8.07	2.84077	8.98332	8.57	2.92746	9.25743	9.07	3.01164	9.52365	9.57	3.09354	9.78264
7.08	2.66083	8.41427	7.58	2.75318	8.70632	8.08	2.84253	8.98888	8.58	2.92916	9.26283	9.08	3.01330	9.52890	9.58	3.09516	9.78775
7.09	2.66271	8.42021	7.59	2.75500	8.71206	8.09	2.84429	8.99444	8.59	2.93087	9.26823	9.09	3.01496	9.53415	9.59	3.09677	9.79285
7.10	2.66458	8.42615	7.60	2.75681	8.71780	8.10	2.84605	9.00000	8.60	2.93258	9.27362	9.10	3.01662	9.53939	9.60	3.09839	9.79796
7.11	2.66646	8.43208	7.61	2.75862	8.72353	8.11	2.84781	9.00555	8.61	2.93428	9.27901	9.11	3.01828	9.54463	9.61	3.10000	9.80306
7.12	2.66833	8.43801	7.62	2.76043	8.72926	8.12	2.84956	9.01110	8.62	2.93598	9.28440	9.12	3.01993	9.54987	9.62	3.10161	9.80816
7.13	2.67021	8.44393	7.63	2.76225	8.73499	8.13	2.85132	9.01665	8.63	2.93769	9.28978	9.13	3.02159	9.55510	9.63	3.10322	9.81326
7.14	2.67208	8.44985	7.64	2.76405	8.74071	8.14	2.85307	9.02219	8.64	2.93939	9.29516	9.14	3.02324	9.56033	9.64	3.10483	9.81835
7.15	2.67395	8.45577	7.65	2.76586	8.74643	8.15	2.85482	9.02774	8.65	2.94109	9.30054	9.15	3.02490	9.56556	9.65	3.10644	9.82344
7.16	2.67582	8.46168	7.66	2.76767	8.75214	8.16	2.85657	9.03327	8.66	2.94279	9.30591	9.16	3.02655	9.57079	9.66	3.10805	9.82853
7.17	2.67769	8.46759	7.67	2.76948	8.75785	8.17	2.85832	9.03881	8.67	2.94449	9.31128	9.17	3.02820	9.57601	9.67	3.10966	9.83362
7.18	2.67955	8.47349	7.68	2.77128	8.76356	8.18	2.86007	9.04434	8.68	2.94618	9.31665	9.18	3.02985	9.58123	9.68	3.11127	9.83870
7.19	2.68142	8.47939	7.69	2.77308	8.76926	8.19	2.86182	9.04986	8.69	2.94788	9.32202	9.19	3.03150	9.58645	9.69	3.11288	9.84378
7.20	2.68328	8.48528	7.70	2.77489	8.77496	8.20	2.86356	9.05539	8.70	2.94958	9.32738	9.20	3.03315	9.59166	9.70	3.11448	9.84886
7.21	2.68514	8.49117	7.71	2.77669	8.78066	8.21	2.86531	9.06091	8.71	2.95127	9.33274	9.21	3.03480	9.59687	9.71	3.11609	9.85393
7.22	2.68701	8.49706	7.72	2.77849	8.78635	8.22	2.86705	9.06642	8.72	2.95296	9.33809	9.22	3.03645	9.60208	9.72	3.11769	9.85901
7.23	2.68887	8.50294	7.73	2.78029	8.79204	8.23	2.86880	9.07193	8.73	2.95466	9.34345	9.23	3.03809	9.60729	9.73	3.11929	9.86408
7.24	2.69072	8.50882	7.74	2.78209	8.79773	8.24	2.87054	9.07744	8.74	2.95635	9.34880	9.24	3.03974	9.61249	9.74	3.12090	9.86914
7.25	2.69258	8.51469	7.75	2.78388	8.80341	8.25	2.87228	9.08295	8.75	2.95804	9.35414	9.25	3.04138	9.61769	9.75	3.12250	9.87421
7.26	2.69444	8.52056	7.76	2.78568	8.80909	8.26	2.87402	9.08845	8.76	2.95973	9.35949	9.26	3.04302	9.62289	9.76	3.12410	9.87927
7.27	2.69629	8.52643	7.77	2.78747	8.81476	8.27	2.87576	9.09395	8.77	2.96142	9.36483	9.27	3.04467	9.62808	9.77	3.12570	9.88433
7.28	2.69815	8.53229	7.78	2.78927	8.82043	8.28	2.87750	9.09945	8.78	2.96311	9.37017	9.28	3.04631	9.63328	9.78	3.12730	9.88939
7.29	2.70000	8.53815	7.79	2.79106	8.82610	8.29	2.87924	9.10494	8.79	2.96479	9.37550	9.29	3.04795	9.63846	9.79	3.12890	9.89444
7.30	2.70185	8.54400	7.80	2.79285	8.83176	8.30	2.88097	9.11043	8.80	2.96648	9.38083	9.30	3.04959	9.64365	9.80	3.13050	9.89949
7.31	2.70370	8.54985	7.81	2.79464	8.83742	8.31	2.88271	9.11592	8.81	2.96816	9.38616	9.31	3.05123	9.64883	9.81	3.13209	9.90454
7.32	2.70555	8.55570	7.82	2.79643	8.84308	8.32	2.88444	9.12140	8.82	2.96985	9.39149	9.32	3.05287	9.65401	9.82	3.13369	9.90959
7.33	2.70740	8.56154	7.83	2.79821	8.84873	8.33	2.88617	9.12688	8.83	2.97153	9.39681	9.33	3.05450	9.65919	9.83	3.13528	9.91464
7.34	2.70924	8.56738	7.84	2.80000	8.85438	8.34	2.88791	9.13236	8.84	2.97321	9.40213	9.34	3.05614	9.66437	9.84	3.13688	9.91968
7.35	2.71109	8.57321	7.85	2.80179	8.86002	8.35	2.88964	9.13783	8.85	2.97489	9.40744	9.35	3.05778	9.66954	9.85	3.13847	9.92472
7.36	2.71293	8.57904	7.86	2.80357	8.86566	8.36	2.89137	9.14330	8.86	2.97658	9.41276	9.36	3.05941	9.67471	9.86	3.14006	9.92975
7.37	2.71477	8.58487	7.87	2.80535	8.87130	8.37	2.89310	9.14877	8.87	2.97825	9.41807	9.37	3.06105	9.67988	9.87	3.14166	9.93479
7.38	2.71662	8.59069	7.88	2.80713	8.87694	8.38	2.89482	9.15423	8.88	2.97993	9.42338	9.38	3.06268	9.68504	9.88	3.14325	9.93982
7.39	2.71846	8.59651	7.89	2.80891	8.88257	8.39	2.89655	9.15969	8.89	2.98161	9.42868	9.39	3.06431	9.69020	9.89	3.14484	9.94485
7.40	2.72029	8.60233	7.90	2.81069	8.88819	8.40	2.89828	9.16515	8.90	2.98329	9.43398	9.40	3.06594	9.69536	9.90	3.14643	9.94987
7.41	2.72213	8.60814	7.91	2.81247	8.89382	8.41	2.90000	9.17061	8.91	2.98496	9.43928	9.41	3.06757	9.70052	9.91	3.14802	9.95490
7.42	2.72397	8.61394	7.92	2.81425	8.89944	8.42	2.90172	9.17606	8.92	2.98664	9.44458	9.42	3.06920	9.70567	9.92	3.14960	9.95992
7.43	2.72580	8.61974	7.93	2.81603	8.90505	8.43	2.90345	9.18150	8.93	2.98831	9.44987	9.43	3.07083	9.71082	9.93	3.15119	9.96494
7.44	2.72764	8.62554	7.94	2.81780	8.91067	8.44	2.90517	9.18695	8.94	2.98998	9.45516	9.44	3.07246	9.71597	9.94	3.15278	9.96995
7.45	2.72947	8.63134	7.95	2.81957	8.91628	8.45	2.90689	9.19239	8.95	2.99166	9.46044	9.45	3.07409	9.72111	9.95	3.15436	9.97497
7.46	2.73130	8.63713	7.96	2.82135	8.92188	8.46	2.90861	9.19783	8.96	2.99333	9.46573	9.46	3.07571	9.72625	9.96	3.15595	9.97998
7.47	2.73313	8.64292	7.97	2.82312	8.92749	8.47	2.91033	9.20326	8.97	2.99500	9.47101	9.47	3.07734	9.73139	9.97	3.15753	9.98499
7.48	2.73496	8.64870	7.98	2.82489	8.93308	8.48	2.91204	9.20869	8.98	2.99666	9.47629	9.48	3.07896	9.73653	9.98	3.15911	9.98999
7.49	2.73679	8.65448	7.99	2.82666	8.93868	8.49	2.91376	9.21412	8.99	2.99833	9.48156	9.49	3.08058	9.74166	9.99	3.16070	9.99500

Appendix IV. The Area under the Normal Curve

This table shows the area under the normal curve between the mean and a selected z value.

Example:

The area under the normal curve between the mean and a z of 1.00 is 0.3413 of the total (34.13 percent of the total). The total area is 1.0.

z/σ	.00	.01	.02	.03	.04	.05	.06	.07	.08	.09
0.0	.0000	.0040	.0080	.0120	.0160	.0199	.0239	.0279	.0319	.0359
0.1	.0398	.0438	.0478	.0517	.0557	.0596	.0636	.0675	.0714	.0753
0.2	.0793	.0832	.0871	.0910	.0948	.0987	.1026	.1064	.1103	.1141
0.3	.1179	.1217	.1255	.1293	.1331	.1368	.1406	.1443	.1480	.1517
0.4	.1554	.1591	.1628	.1664	.1700	.1736	.1772	.1808	.1844	.1879
0.5	.1915	.1950	.1985	.2019	.2054	.2088	.2123	.2157	.2190	.2224
0.6	.2257	.2291	.2324	.2357	.2389	.2422	.2454	.2486	.2518	.2549
0.7	.2580	.2612	.2642	.2673	.2704	.2734	.2764	.2794	.2823	.2852
0.8	.2881	.2910	.2939	.2967	.2995	.3023	.3051	.3078	.3106	.3133
0.9	.3159	.3186	.3212	.3238	.3264	.3289	.3315	.3340	.3365	.3389
1.0	.3413	.3438	.3461	.3485	.3508	.3531	.3554	.3577	.3599	.3621
1.1	.3643	.3665	.3686	.3708	.3729	.3749	.3770	.3790	.3810	.3830
1.2	.3849	.3869	.3888	.3907	.3925	.3944	.3962	.3980	.3997	.4015
1.3	.4032	.4049	.4066	.4082	.4099	.4115	.4131	.4147	.4162	.4177
1.4	.4192	.4207	.4222	.4236	.4251	.4265	.4279	.4292	.4306	.4319
1.5	.4332	.4345	.4357	.4370	.4382	.4394	.4406	.4418	.4429	.4441
1.6	.4452	.4463	.4474	.4484	.4495	.4505	.4515	.4525	.4535	.4545
1.7	.4554	.4564	.4573	.4582	.4591	.4599	.4608	.4616	.4625	.4633
1.8	.4641	.4649	.4656	.4664	.4671	.4678	.4686	.4693	.4699	.4706
1.9	.4713	.4719	.4726	.4732	.4738	.4744	.4750	.4756	.4761	.4767
2.0	.4772	.4778	.4783	.4788	.4793	.4798	.4803	.4808	.4812	.4817
2.1	.4821	.4826	.4830	.4834	.4838	.4842	.4846	.4850	.4854	.4857
2.2	.4861	.4864	.4868	.4871	.4875	.4878	.4881	.4884	.4887	.4890
2.3	.4893	.4896	.4898	.4901	.4904	.4906	.4909	.4911	.4913	.4916
2.4	.4918	.4920	.4922	.4925	.4927	.4929	.4931	.4932	.4934	.4936
2.5	.4938	.4940	.4941	.4943	.4945	.4946	.4948	.4949	.4951	.4952
2.6	.4953	.4955	.4956	.4957	.4959	.4960	.4961	.4962	.4963	.4964
2.7	.4965	.4966	.4967	.4968	.4969	.4970	.4971	.4972	.4973	.4974
2.8	.4974	.4975	.4976	.4977	.4977	.4978	.4979	.4979	.4980	.4981
2.9	.4981	.4982	.4982	.4983	.4984	.4984	.4985	.4985	.4986	.4986
3.0	.49865	.4987	.4987	.4988	.4988	.4989	.4989	.4989	.4990	.4990
3.1	.49903	.4991	.4991	.4991	.4992	.4992	.4992	.4992	.4993	.4993
3.2	.4993129	.4993	.4994	.4994	.4994	.4994	.4994	.4995	.4995	.4995
3.3	.4995166	.4995	.4995	.4996	.4996	.4996	.4996	.4996	.4996	.4997
3.4	.4996631	.4997	.4997	.4997	.4997	.4997	.4997	.4997	.4998	.4998
3.5	.4997674	.4998	.4998	.4998	.4998	.4998	.4998	.4998	.4998	.4998
3.6	.4998409	.4998	.4999	.4999	.4999	.4999	.4999	.4999	.4999	.4999
3.7	.4998922	.4999	.4999	.4999	.4999	.4999	.4999	.4999	.4999	.4999
3.8	.4999277	.4999	.4999	.4999	.4999	.4999	.4999	.5000	.5000	.4999
3.9	.4999519	.5000	.5000	.5000	.5000	.5000	.5000	.5000	.5000	.5000
4.0	.4999683									
4.5	.4999966									
5.0	.4999997133									

Appendix V. Critical Values of Chi-Square

Example: The number on the χ^2 scale for 10 d.f. corresponding to the area of 0.05 in the one tail is 18.3.

d/f	0.30	0.20	0.10	0.05	0.025	0.010	0.005	0.001
1	1.07	1.64	2.71	3.84	5.02	6.63	7.88	10.8
2	2.41	3.22	4.61	5.99	7.38	9.21	10.6	13.8
3	3.67	4.64	6.25	7.82	9.35	11.3	12.8	16.3
4	4.88	5.99	7.78	9.49	11.1	13.3	14.9	18.5
5	6.06	7.29	9.24	11.1	12.8	15.1	16.7	20.5
6	7.23	8.56	10.6	12.6	14.4	16.8	18.5	22.5
7	8.38	9.80	12.0	14.1	16.0	18.5	20.3	24.3
8	9.52	11.0	13.4	15.5	17.5	20.1	22.0	26.1
9	10.7	12.2	14.7	16.9	19.0	21.7	23.6	27.9
10	11.8	13.4	16.0	18.3	20.5	23.2	25.2	29.6
11	12.9	14.6	17.3	19.7	21.9	24.7	26.8	31.3
12	14.0	15.8	18.5	21.0	23.3	26.2	28.3	32.9
13	15.1	17.0	19.8	22.4	24.7	27.7	29.8	34.5
14	16.2	18.2	21.1	23.7	26.1	29.1	31.3	36.1
15	17.3	19.3	22.3	25.0	27.5	30.6	32.8	37.7
16	18.4	20.5	23.5	26.3	28.8	32.0	34.3	39.3
17	19.5	21.6	24.8	27.6	30.2	33.4	35.7	40.8
18	20.6	22.8	26.0	28.9	31.5	34.8	37.2	42.3
19	21.7	23.9	27.2	30.1	32.9	36.2	38.6	43.8
20	22.8	25.0	28.4	31.4	34.2	37.6	40.0	45.3
21	23.9	26.2	29.6	32.7	35.5	38.9	41.4	46.8
22	24.9	27.3	30.8	33.9	36.8	40.3	42.8	48.3
23	26.0	28.4	32.0	35.2	38.1	41.6	44.2	49.7
24	27.1	29.6	33.2	36.4	39.4	43.0	45.6	51.2
25	28.2	30.7	34.4	37.7	40.8	44.3	46.9	52.6
26	29.2	31.8	35.6	38.9	41.9	45.6	48.3	54.1
27	30.3	32.9	36.7	40.1	43.2	47.0	49.6	55.5
28	31.4	34.0	37.9	41.3	44.5	48.3	51.0	56.9
29	32.5	35.1	39.1	42.6	45.7	49.6	52.3	58.3
30	33.5	36.3	40.3	43.8	47.0	50.9	53.7	59.7

Source: Catherine M. Thompson, "Tables of the Percentage Points of the χ^2 Distribution," *Biometrika*, Vol. XXXII (1941), pp. 188–89. The remainder of the table is abridged with permission from Table IV of R. A. Fisher and F. Yates, *Statistical Tables for Biological, Agricultural and Medical Research* (Edinburgh: Oliver & Boyd, Ltd.).

Appendix VI. The Poisson Distribution

Values in the table are for the function:

$$P(x) = \frac{\mu^x e^{-\mu}}{x(x-1)(x-2)\cdots 1}$$

$P(x)$ for specified values of μ

x	$\mu=0.1$	$\mu=0.2$	$\mu=0.3$	$\mu=0.4$	$\mu=0.5$	$\mu=0.6$	$\mu=0.7$	$\mu=0.8$	$\mu=0.9$	$\mu=1.0$
0	.9048374	.8187308	.7408182	.6703200	.606531	.548812	.496585	.449329	.406570	.367879
1	.0904837	.1637462	.2222455	.2681280	.303265	.329287	.347610	.359463	.365913	.367879
2	.0045242	.0163746	.0333368	.0536256	.075816	.098786	.121663	.143785	.164661	.183940
3	.0001508	.0010916	.0033337	.0071501	.012636	.019757	.028388	.038343	.049398	.061313
4	.0000038	.0000546	.0002500	.0007150	.001580	.002964	.004968	.007669	.011115	.015328
5	.0000001	.0000022	.0000150	.0000572	.000158	.000356	.000696	.001227	.002001	.003066
6		.0000001	.0000008	.0000038	.000013	.000036	.000081	.000164	.000300	.000511
7				.0000002	.000001	.000003	.000008	.000019	.000039	.000073
8							.000001	.000002	.000004	.000009
9										.000001

x	$\mu=2.0$	$\mu=3.0$	$\mu=4.0$	$\mu=5.0$	$\mu=6.0$	$\mu=7.0$	$\mu=8.0$	$\mu=9.0$	$\mu=10.0$
0	.135335	.049787	.018316	.006738	.002479	.000912	.000335	.000123	.000045
1	.270671	.149361	.073263	.033690	.014873	.006383	.002684	.001111	.000454
2	.270671	.224042	.146525	.084224	.044618	.022341	.010735	.004998	.002270
3	.180447	.224042	.195367	.140374	.089235	.052129	.028626	.014994	.007567
4	.090224	.168031	.195367	.175467	.133853	.091226	.057252	.033737	.018917
5	.036089	.100819	.156293	.175467	.160623	.127717	.091604	.060727	.037833
6	.012030	.050409	.104196	.146223	.160623	.149003	.122138	.091090	.063055
7	.003437	.021604	.059540	.104445	.137677	.149003	.139587	.117116	.090079
8	.000859	.008102	.029770	.065278	.103258	.130377	.139587	.131756	.112599
9	.000191	.002701	.013231	.036266	.068838	.101405	.124077	.131756	.125110
10	.000038	.000810	.005292	.018133	.041303	.070983	.099263	.118580	.125110
11	.000007	.000221	.001925	.008242	.022529	.045171	.072190	.097020	.113736
12	.000001	.000055	.000642	.003434	.011264	.026350	.048127	.072765	.094780
13		.000013	.000197	.001321	.005199	.014188	.029616	.050376	.072908
14		.000003	.000056	.000472	.002228	.007094	.016924	.032384	.052077
15		.000001	.000015	.000157	.000891	.003311	.009026	.019431	.034718
16			.000004	.000049	.000334	.001448	.004513	.010930	.021699
17			.000001	.000014	.000118	.000596	.002124	.005786	.012764
18				.000004	.000039	.000232	.000944	.002893	.007091
19				.000001	.000012	.000085	.000397	.001370	.003732
20					.000004	.000030	.000159	.000617	.001866
21					.000001	.000010	.000061	.000264	.000889
22						.000003	.000022	.000108	.000404
23						.000001	.000008	.000042	.000176
24							.000003	.000016	.000073
25							.000001	.000006	.000029
26								.000002	.000011
27								.000001	.000004
28									.000001
29									.000001

Source: E. C. Molina, *Poisson's Exponential Binomial Limit* (Princeton, N.J.: D. Van Nostrand Co., Inc., 1942). Reprinted by permission.

Appendix VII. Binomial Distribution

$$P\{r\} = \frac{n!}{r!(n-r)!}\, p^r q^{n-r}$$

n	r	.05	.10	.15	.20	.25	.30 (P)	.35	.40	.45	.50
1	0	.9500	.9000	.8500	.8000	.7500	.7000	.6500	.6000	.5500	.5000
	1	.0500	.1000	.1500	.2000	.2500	.3000	.3500	.4000	.4500	.5000
2	0	.9025	.8100	.7225	.6400	.5625	.4900	.4225	.3600	.3025	.2500
	1	.0950	.1800	.2550	.3200	.3750	.4200	.4550	.4800	.4950	.5000
	2	.0025	.0100	.0225	.0400	.0625	.0900	.1225	.1600	.2025	.2500
3	0	.8574	.7290	.6141	.5120	.4219	.3430	.2746	.2160	.1664	.1250
	1	.1354	.2430	.3251	.3840	.4219	.4410	.4436	.4320	.4084	.3750
	2	.0071	.0270	.0574	.0960	.1406	.1890	.2389	.2880	.3341	.3750
	3	.0001	.0010	.0034	.0080	.0156	.0270	.0429	.0640	.0911	.1250
4	0	.8145	.6561	.5220	.4096	.3164	.2401	.1785	.1296	.0915	.0625
	1	.1715	.2916	.3685	.4096	.4219	.4116	.3845	.3456	.2995	.2500
	2	.0135	.0486	.0975	.1536	.2109	.2646	.3105	.3456	.3675	.3750
	3	.0005	.0036	.0115	.0256	.0469	.0756	.1115	.1536	.2005	.2500
	4	.0000	.0001	.0005	.0016	.0039	.0081	.0150	.0256	.0410	.0625
5	0	.7738	.5905	.4437	.3277	.2373	.1681	.1160	.0778	.0503	.0312
	1	.2036	.3280	.3915	.4096	.3955	.3602	.3124	.2592	.2059	.1562
	2	.0214	.0729	.1382	.2048	.2637	.3087	.3364	.3456	.3369	.3125
	3	.0011	.0081	.0244	.0512	.0879	.1323	.1811	.2304	.2757	.3125
	4	.0000	.0004	.0022	.0064	.0146	.0284	.0488	.0768	.1128	.1562
	5	.0000	.0000	.0001	.0003	.0010	.0024	.0053	.0102	.0185	.0312
6	0	.7351	.5314	.3771	.2621	.1780	.1176	.0754	.0467	.0277	.0156
	1	.2321	.3543	.3993	.3932	.3560	.3025	.2437	.1866	.1359	.0938
	2	.0305	.0984	.1762	.2458	.2966	.3241	.3280	.3110	.2780	.2344
	3	.0021	.0146	.0415	.0819	.1318	.1852	.2355	.2765	.3032	.3125
	4	.0001	.0012	.0055	.0154	.0330	.0595	.0951	.1382	.1861	.2344
	5	.0000	.0001	.0004	.0015	.0044	.0102	.0205	.0369	.0609	.0938
	6	.0000	.0000	.0000	.0001	.0002	.0007	.0018	.0041	.0083	.0156
7	0	.6983	.4783	.3206	.2097	.1335	.0824	.0490	.0280	.0152	.0078
	1	.2573	.3720	.3960	.3670	.3115	.2471	.1848	.1306	.0872	.0547
	2	.0406	.1240	.2097	.2753	.3115	.3177	.2985	.2613	.2140	.1641
	3	.0036	.0230	.0617	.1147	.1730	.2269	.2679	.2903	.2918	.2734
	4	.0002	.0026	.0109	.0287	.0577	.0972	.1442	.1935	.2388	.2734
	5	.0000	.0002	.0012	.0043	.0115	.0250	.0466	.0774	.1172	.1641
	6	.0000	.0000	.0001	.0004	.0013	.0036	.0084	.0172	.0320	.0547
	7	.0000	.0000	.0000	.0000	.0001	.0002	.0006	.0016	.0037	.0078
8	0	.6634	.4305	.2725	.1678	.1002	.0576	.0319	.0168	.0084	.0039
	1	.2793	.3826	.3847	.3355	.2670	.1977	.1373	.0896	.0548	.0312
	2	.0515	.1488	.2376	.2936	.3115	.2965	.2587	.2090	.1569	.1094
	3	.0054	.0331	.0839	.1468	.2076	.2541	.2786	.2787	.2568	.2188
	4	.0004	.0046	.0185	.0459	.0865	.1361	.1875	.2322	.2627	.2734
	5	.0000	.0004	.0026	.0092	.0231	.0467	.0808	.1239	.1719	.2188
	6	.0000	.0000	.0002	.0011	.0038	.0100	.0217	.0413	.0703	.1094
	7	.0000	.0000	.0000	.0001	.0004	.0012	.0033	.0079	.0164	.0312
	8	.0000	.0000	.0000	.0000	.0000	.0001	.0002	.0007	.0017	.0039
9	0	.6302	.3874	.2316	.1342	.0751	.0404	.0207	.0101	.0046	.0020
	1	.2985	.3874	.3679	.3020	.2253	.1556	.1004	.0605	.0339	.0176
	2	.0629	.1722	.2597	.3020	.3003	.2668	.2162	.1612	.1110	.0703
	3	.0077	.0446	.1069	.1762	.2336	.2668	.2716	.2508	.2119	.1641
	4	.0006	.0074	.0283	.0661	.1168	.1715	.2194	.2508	.2600	.2461
	5	.0000	.0008	.0050	.0165	.0389	.0735	.1181	.1672	.2128	.2461
	6	.0000	.0001	.0006	.0028	.0087	.0210	.0424	.0743	.1160	.1641
	7	.0000	.0000	.0000	.0003	.0012	.0039	.0098	.0212	.0407	.0703
	8	.0000	.0000	.0000	.0000	.0001	.0004	.0013	.0035	.0083	.0176
	9	.0000	.0000	.0000	.0000	.0000	.0000	.0001	.0003	.0008	.0020
10	0	.5987	.3487	.1969	.1074	.0563	.0282	.0135	.0060	.0025	.0010
	1	.3151	.3874	.3474	.2684	.1877	.1211	.0725	.0403	.0207	.0098
	2	.0746	.1937	.2759	.3020	.2816	.2335	.1757	.1209	.0763	.0439
	3	.0105	.0574	.1298	.2013	.2503	.2668	.2522	.2150	.1665	.1172
	4	.0010	.0112	.0401	.0881	.1460	.2001	.2377	.2508	.2384	.2051
	5	.0001	.0015	.0085	.0264	.0584	.1029	.1536	.2007	.2340	.2461
	6	.0000	.0001	.0012	.0055	.0162	.0368	.0689	.1115	.1596	.2051
	7	.0000	.0000	.0001	.0008	.0031	.0090	.0212	.0425	.0746	.1172
	8	.0000	.0000	.0000	.0001	.0004	.0014	.0043	.0106	.0229	.0439
	9	.0000	.0000	.0000	.0000	.0000	.0001	.0005	.0016	.0042	.0098
	10	.0000	.0000	.0000	.0000	.0000	.0000	.0000	.0001	.0003	.0010
11	0	.5688	.3138	.1673	.0859	.0422	.0198	.0088	.0036	.0014	.0005
	1	.3293	.3835	.3248	.2362	.1549	.0932	.0518	.0266	.0125	.0054
	2	.0867	.2131	.2866	.2953	.2581	.1998	.1395	.0887	.0513	.0269
	3	.0137	.0710	.1517	.2215	.2581	.2568	.2254	.1774	.1259	.0806
	4	.0014	.0158	.0536	.1107	.1721	.2201	.2428	.2365	.2060	.1611
	5	.0001	.0025	.0132	.0388	.0803	.1321	.1830	.2207	.2360	.2256
	6	.0000	.0003	.0023	.0097	.0268	.0566	.0985	.1471	.1931	.2256
	7	.0000	.0000	.0003	.0017	.0064	.0173	.0379	.0701	.1128	.1611
	8	.0000	.0000	.0000	.0002	.0011	.0037	.0102	.0234	.0462	.0806
	9	.0000	.0000	.0000	.0000	.0001	.0005	.0018	.0052	.0126	.0269
	10	.0000	.0000	.0000	.0000	.0000	.0000	.0002	.0007	.0021	.0054
	11	.0000	.0000	.0000	.0000	.0000	.0000	.0000	.0000	.0002	.0005

Source: Extracted from "Tables of the Binomial Probability Distribution," U.S. Department of Commerce, National Bureau of Standards, Applied Mathematics Series 6 (1952).

Index

This book has been set in 10 and 9 point Times Roman, leaded 2 points. Chapter numbers are in 16 and 30 point Helvetica and chapter titles are in 18 point Helvetica Medium. The size of the type page is 42 x 52½ picas.